UTAH

OFFICIAL STATS

NAME: Kenneth Gerrard

VITALS: Age: 34
                     Height: 6'2"
                     Eye Color: Green
                     Hair: Dark brown, on the
                     long side

OCCUPATION: Attorney

OBJECTIVE: To win back the woman
                     he lost fifteen years
                     earlier when he entered
                     the witness protection
                     program. The catch—he
                     can't tell her his identity.
                     He must keep intact his
                     new look and new life or
                     his family will be
                     endangered.

ADDITIONAL INFO: Once an intense,
                     passionate bad boy, he's
                     now a man of honor and
                     incredible character with
                     a heart to match.

DANGEROUS TO LOVE

DANGEROUS TO LOVE
USA

BONNIE K. WINN
WHEN A MAN LOVES A WOMAN

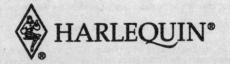

HARLEQUIN®

TORONTO • NEW YORK • LONDON
AMSTERDAM • PARIS • SYDNEY • HAMBURG
STOCKHOLM • ATHENS • TOKYO • MILAN • MADRID
PRAGUE • WARSAW • BUDAPEST • AUCKLAND

To my editor, Bonnie Crisalli,
for working with me to bring this story to life
and for being ever so patient as it came to term.

To Karen Rigley and Karen Sims,
for your friendship and your invaluable assistance.

HARLEQUIN BOOKS
225 Duncan Mill Road, Don Mills,
Ontario, Canada M3B 3K9

ISBN 0-373-82342-8

WHEN A MAN LOVES A WOMAN

Copyright © 1996 by Bonnie K. Winn

BONNIE K. WINN

Being a hopeless romantic, and having written incessantly since the third grade, it seemed only natural that Bonnie K. Winn turned to romance writing. A seasoned author of historical and contemporary romance, her bestselling books have won numerous awards. *Affaire de Coeur* chose her as one of the Top Ten Romance Authors in America.

Bonnie loves writing contemporary romance because she can set her stories in the modern cities close to her heart and explore the endlessly fascinating strengths of today's woman.

Living in the foothills of the Rockies gives her plenty of inspiration and a touch of whimsy, as well. She shares her life with her husband, son and a spunky Westie terrier who lends his characteristics to many pets in her stories. Bonnie's keeping mum about anyone else's characteristics she may have borrowed.

Books by Bonnie K. Winn

Harlequin American Romance

The Newlywed Game #624
When a Man Loves a Woman #646
The Daddy Factor #680
His-and-Hers Family #720
The Accidental Mrs. Mackenzie #775
The Mommy Makeover #812

Steeple Hill Love Inspired

A Family All Her Own #158
Family Ties #186

Silhouette Intimate Moments

The Hijacked Wife #954

Harlequin Superromance

The Wrong Brother #898
Family Found #964

Dear Reader,

If you're like me, you've felt the joy, wonder and yes, even pain of a first incomparable love. In conceiving this book, my thoughts turned to the path our heart takes if that love ends. Sometimes it seems impossible to move beyond what is gone. Especially if we believe that singular person is our destiny...our soul mate, the only one who completes us.

But what if we get the opportunity to relive the relationship? Can destiny conquer the past? Or are second chances as random as fate? Please join me on this journey of discovery, danger...and desire.

I hope you'll enjoy the ride.

Warmly,

Bonnie K. Winn

Please address questions and book requests to:
Harlequin Reader Service
U.S.: 3010 Walden Ave., P.O. Box 1325, Buffalo, NY 14269
Canadian: P.O. Box 609, Fort Erie, Ont. L2A 5X3

Chapter One

This was it. A lifetime of preparation for the case that could make or break her career. Barbara Callister drew in a discreet breath for reassurance as she smoothed the impeccable camel-colored wool of her severely tailored suit, then pushed open the door to the courtroom. She'd checked and rechecked every detail—from each line of every document resting inside her briefcase to the raw silk blouse that softened her power suit.

Barrett and Barrett could send out every top gun in their arsenal and they wouldn't catch her unprepared. She scanned the crowd, wondering which one of the "suits" was the infamous Kenneth Gerrard, the barracuda sent from the San Francisco legal office to outpower the local legal talent. Barbara, along with the partners in her firm, Coker and Rigley, had been surprised by the turn of events.

She'd been assigned this case because she was good—one of Salt Lake City's best litigators. But no one in her firm had expected the opposition to call in a high-powered litigator from out of town. Expecting once this news broke to have to relinquish the case to one of the senior partners, Barbara had been amazed to find they still wanted her to represent Coker & Rigley in the case of the decade. Corporate litigation was her specialty and she sensed this case could propel her forward on the partnership track sooner than she anticipated.

A whirlwind of barely contained energy honed to fighting form, Barbara moved with confidence through the crowded courtroom. She found she was anticipating this match. Gerrard might be good, but she planned to be better. She took a deep breath as she looked around the room. *At least she hoped she would be.*

Gripping her briefcase, she wove through the spectators, headed for the plaintiff's table. As always when intensely concentrating, she saw little other than the direct path in front of her. But that path ended quickly when an overpowering, distinctly male form blocked her way.

She looked up to see who had so rudely moved to obstruct the aisle, a caustic comment already forming, but it died away as she met twinkling green eyes. Coupled with a grinning mouth beneath a well-groomed mustache that indented charmingly in a face that made the most of hard planes and edges, it was a knockout combination. One that touched some forgotten chord before she nudged the thought aside.

One eyebrow rose as he made a slow appraisal from the top of her midnight-colored hair to the tips of her high-heeled kidskin pumps. And his expression made it clear he was pleased with the entire package.

She resisted the urge to respond in kind. Now was a time for business. Nothing else. Not even for the most attractive man she'd stumbled across in far longer than she wanted to count. She smiled to take the sting from her words. "One aisle per person. And I believe this one's mine."

He moved aside, allowing her to pass, but his gaze remained trained on her departing form. "The view just gets better."

Angling her head back, she saw the admiration painted on his features. At some other time she probably would have appreciated his casual good looks, the confidence that emanated from him as naturally as his cocky grin. But not now. Despite a bracing dose of courage, she was keyed-up about this case.

Sending the man a distracted smile, she slid into place and greeted her client. As she snapped open her briefcase, she again ignored the niggling feelings that persisted as she thought of the good-looking stranger. Carefully she lifted out her notes and a legal pad, making sure her exhibits were lined up in precise fashion.

Barbara checked her watch, noting that it was five minutes until court time. Judge Donald Herbert was punctual to a fault. Unfortunately her associate and harebrained friend Dani wasn't. If not for her legal brilliance, Barbara would have opted for someone else to sit this trial, but Dani, despite her faults, was the best.

With seconds remaining, Dani slid into the chair next to Barbara's, her winsome smile in place beneath a riot of strawberry curls and flushed cheeks. "Hi! Got the courtroom number mixed up. Thank God I beat Horrible Herbert."

Barbara restrained the desire to strangle Dani as

they both rose at the judge's entrance. There was no room in this case for error and the thought of dueling with a high-powered litigator was making her more anxious than usual. Glancing at opposing counsel's table, Barbara's jaw nearly dropped as she saw the flirtatious stranger manning that very table.

Momentarily forgetting etiquette, she hissed into Dani's ear, "Who is that?"

Dani's gaze followed hers, her lips quirking into a satisfied grin. "That, my dear, is *the* Kenneth Gerrard."

Barbara withheld her reaction. Spared from meeting him before the trial, she hadn't any idea.... Dani had done all the prediscovery work conducted in San Francisco and Gerrard had sent competent associates to the Salt Lake office, one of whom was sitting at the table with him now. Barbara's communications with Gerrard had been by mail or fax. Throat dry, she wondered how she'd stand being seated opposite the Armani-clad Adonis for the duration of the trial.

Suddenly aware of Dani digging a sharp elbow into her side, Barbara dragged her gaze away from Kenneth Gerrard and stared up at the judge.

"*Miss Callister,*" the judge repeated with exaggerated patience. "If I can have your attention, we will begin jury selection now."

"Yes, sir," she mumbled, acutely embarrassed by her unprofessional behavior.

"He's a hunk," Dani whispered, "but not worth blowing the case over."

Barbara straightened up and fiddled with the legal pad, positioning it carefully so as not to let her gaze wander. Taking notes on the first prospective juror, she found her usually unshakable concentration fading as her eyes slid to the defendant's table. There was something about Kenneth Gerrard, something she couldn't put her finger on....

"*Miss Callister,* are we keeping you from something else?" the judge questioned, pushing his half glasses down his nose, the skin on his bald head shining beneath the unforgiving courtroom lights.

Barbara flushed. "No, sir. That is…I'm ready to question the juror."

"That's fine, but Mr. Gerrard has already struck him. Call the next name on your list."

Dani's eyes were wide with concern, and Barbara called on the poise that she'd cultivated over fifteen years. For the next few hours, furious with herself, she gave new definition to concentration. She wasn't a hormonal teenager, easily thrown by an attractive man…no matter how handsome.

When the judge adjourned the proceedings for the day, Barbara gathered her papers with a vengeance. She planned to spend the night going over the notes she and Dani had made, making sure she hadn't missed anything during her ridiculous daydreaming.

"Miss Callister." Kenneth Gerrard's smooth voice glided over her.

Her spine automatically stiffened. "I think it's a bit late for introductions."

His smile was as smooth as his voice. "You didn't seem interested earlier."

"And I'm not interested now," she retorted, embarrassed by her behavior and mortified that he hadn't clarified his identity.

"Perhaps we should have all worn ID tags," he

suggested, that smile still lurking, just waiting to turn up his delicious-looking lips.

She wanted to chuckle at the ridiculousness of the suggestion, the frank smile that said he knew she was peeved. But she still felt too embarrassed to appreciate his levity. One brush with blowing the case was enough. She snapped her briefcase shut dismissively. "And perhaps you could have remembered your manners earlier."

"Then let me make it up to you now. How about a drink?"

Shock overrode caution. From his reputation she hadn't expected him to be the type to break the rules. "I don't think so. *I* have my client's interests to consider."

His brow winged upward again. "I doubt either of our clients would mind your pointing me in the direction of a drink. I promise not to photograph everything in your attaché case."

Her gaze slid downward toward her briefcase before she snapped her eyes back up to meet his, caught again by something she saw there. Her gaze lingered on the sculpted waves of chestnut hair, then drifted over his handsome features, yet she steeled herself to sound uninterested. "Funny. But I'll have to pass." Not allowing herself to say more, she pivoted and exited the courtroom.

"A pity," he muttered to no one in particular. The twinkle in his eyes faded along with his grin, replaced by longing and a shred of pain he'd never quite conquered. Some lark. He should have had his head examined for thinking he could simply look and then walk away. A yawning emptiness reminded him that it was impossible to let go of some things.

Things like Barbara Callister.

But she had left before seeing the conflicting emotions covering his face, the disappointment coupled with something far deeper. Something he'd never quite been able to forget.

LINGERING TENDRILS of sunshine greeted Barbara and she breathed in deeply, relieved to be outside. Normally relief was a rare sensation. Usually she felt a letdown when leaving the courthouse, preferring the battle to the intermissions. Until lately...

"Barb, wait up." Dani danced down the steps and into unison with Barbara's long-legged stride. "We still on for tonight?"

"Sure." Now that she was outside the courtroom she could relax. Flashing Dani a wide grin, Barbara eased her killer pace. "I'm sorry. Just had a lot on my mind."

"Yeah, like that yummy Kenneth Gerrard."

Barbara mumbled something unintelligible, but distinctly unflattering.

"Maybe good looks are a requirement to get hired at Barrett and Barrett. Did you see how cute his associate is?" Dani's voice turned dreamy. "Brian Thomas. Even his name sounds cute. Maybe not as overpowering as Gerrard, but definitely high on the appeal scale."

Barbara had barely noticed the other man. Something about Kenneth Gerrard overwhelmed anyone else. "If you say so. But then you're obsessed," she teased. "I have to peel you off the screen every time there's a rerun of a Costner movie."

Dani remained unperturbed. "Let's go to my place, order pizza, get crazy, attack some Häagen-Dazs or even the pizza guy if he's cute."

Barbara felt the laughter float upward. It was the effect Dani always had on her. "Think we can fit some work into the evening?"

"Sure." Her tone turned to one of mock reproof. "Even though *I'm* not the one mooning over opposing counsel instead of paying attention."

"Which is something we're going to talk about." Barbara pinned Dani with a knowing gaze. "Why were you holding out about Gerrard?"

Dani smiled mischievously. "I wondered how long it was going to take you to nail me on that."

Barbara lifted one eyebrow. "Not long, my friend. And you've got a whole pizza, not to mention the delivery guy, to come clean."

AN EMPTY PIZZA CARTON and a demolished quart of Chocolate Chocolate Chip ice cream littered the already cluttered table in Dani's dining room.

Barbara wrinkled her nose as she pushed aside a pile of dog-eared magazines and a coffee-stained collection of letters and junk mail. "Doesn't this… uh…stuff ever bother you?"

Dani shrugged. "Not everybody likes a sterile environment. You could do with some loosening up yourself, kid."

Instead of a witty retort, Barbara stared out the wall-size windows at the lights of the valley twinkling below. "Yeah, I know."

Dani screwed her face into a puzzled question mark. "Excuse me. Has someone kidnapped the real Barbara Callister and left her winsome clone?" Her snapping cinnamon eyes narrowed. "Invasion of the body snatchers. It had to happen."

Barbara threw a colorful, if somewhat ragged, pillow at her.

"What gives, Barb?" Dani's face cleared as her tone grew knowing. "Could it be that Barbie has finally met her Ken? In the form of the gorgeous Kenneth Gerrard?"

"Don't be ridiculous. That's not what he's looking for." His type wasn't looking for anything that permanent. Barbara tossed the notes on the table, rising to pad to the window. "It's just that..."

"What?" Dani prompted.

"Do you ever wonder? I mean about something in your past. Something that if you could change, it might mean your life would have been completely different." Barbara fingered the drapery cord as she stared into the darkness, thinking of a long-ago night.

"I take it this involves another person," Dani guessed correctly as she sipped a diet Coke.

Barbara shifted restlessly. "I know my career's on track. I'm facing the greatest case ever. It's just that something's missing...."

"Like a husband, maybe a few kids?" Dani suggested practically.

Barbara wanted to protest, but Dani had struck the mark with disturbing accuracy. Her voice softened reflectively. "I was going to get married once."

Dani sat up, her interest heightened. "And?"

"I was nineteen." Barbara laughed softly. "God,

that sounds like a lifetime ago. His name was Billy Duncan. I've never loved anyone so much. We planned to get married.''

"But?"

"We had a stupid fight. He wanted to elope. I worried about losing my scholarship. I wouldn't have had enough money to keep attending Rice University, but he didn't understand since his family footed all the bills for him. And I knew my family would want me to have a formal wedding—''

"All the practicalities. That's the Barb we know and love,'' Dani filled in. "You couldn't make up?''

"We never got the chance. He said elope or nothing. I guess he meant it.''

"You didn't try to see him again?''

Barbara nodded, seeing the lights of the city spread out beneath her like fairy dust. "Actually I did. He stood me up the next day. I thought he was sore and would get over it. I let him stew for a few days, then went looking for him.'' Barbara met Dani's face, smiling sadly. "He'd disappeared and no one in his frat house knew where he'd gone.''

"That's kind of strange, don't you think?''

"Not as strange as finding out his entire family had moved, which in retrospect is probably why he was pushing so hard to elope that night. I kept hoping he'd call or write. But he didn't.''

"And now you're wondering what would have happened if you'd thrown caution to the wind and eloped with him?''

Barbara hesitated, then nodded. "There's never been anyone else like him.'' A wistful look crossed her face. "He could always make me laugh. Being the class clown will do that, I suppose, but he was so on fire for life. It was magic just being with him.''

"Have you thought about trying to find him now?" Dani questioned. "Hire a private investigator. They do it all the time on 'Oprah.'"

"Life's not a talk show," Barbara responded, unable to repress a small note of longing. "Coming face-to-face with the woman he's no doubt married, the beautiful blue-eyed babies they'd have…''

"Ones that could have been yours."

Barbara grimaced. "Ouch, William Tell. You do hit what you aim for."

"Just an observation. Who hasn't hit thirty and wondered what could have been?"

"It's been fifteen years," Barbara mused, thinking of the intense but joyous young Billy Duncan. Wild, longish sun-streaked blond hair had surrounded a face that seldom knew anything but laughter. The arrogant stance, the small diamond stud in one ear that flashed with the lightninglike movements of his head. Whipcord slim, he'd held her with a passion that defied the laughter they shared. Rice University with its cache of wild-eyed liberals and eccentric intellectuals had been their playground. One that she'd let slip away. What if she had shed caution, said yes…? Her life would be different. So very, very different.

Glancing at Dani's concerned face, Barbara managed a smile. "I didn't mean to go all maudlin on you. Guess my biological clock went into an unscheduled spin."

Dani shrugged it off. "We're all allowed. But maybe destiny's knocking on your door again."

Barbara frowned in puzzlement.

"Kenneth Gerrard. I haven't seen you so taken with a man in..." Dani's pixie face screwed into a knot of concentration. "I guess I've never seen you so taken with a man."

"Please, Dani. I'm not so desperate that I'm willing to sleep with the enemy."

Dani lifted expressive eyebrows. "Hey, now there's a punishment I'd sign up for in a heartbeat. And I don't think he's cruising for the desperate, if you know what I mean."

Barbara knew exactly what she meant. Tall, athletically muscular with drop dead, polished *GQ* looks, Kenneth Gerrard hardly needed to settle. "Just because he stunned me for a minute—"

"Tsk, tsk. I was there, remember? You acted like someone drained your carburetor."

Barbara remembered the unsettling feeling he'd caused, but deliberately shrugged away the memory. "He's good...okay, great-looking. But that's all. It was temporary insanity, nothing else. Don't bring destiny into this."

Dani grinned. "Counselor, there's not a court in the land that would let you cop that plea."

BARBARA SWUNG OPEN the door to her apartment, disturbed by the yawning silence. Kicking off her heels, she glanced with disinterest at the flashing light on her answering machine. No one she cared about would have called.

She caught her breath at that unexpected thought. How long had it been since her heart had raced at the thought of someone's call? Even though it had been fifteen years since she'd stormed away from Billy, refusing to elope, she hadn't given her heart to anyone else.

And now something was missing.

Critical eyes assessed the impeccably furnished apartment. Cream-colored leather couches dominated the living room, brass-and-glass tables were placed strategically to hold her porcelain collection. Miles of even lighter cream carpet lay thickly underfoot. Navy brocade throw pillows rested easily near a navy-and-burgundy wall hanging, relieving the sensation of stepping into a nearly white oasis.

Luxurious, tastefully decorated, it once had been an important source of pride. Especially since she'd worked, sacrificing her personal life, to earn a salary that allowed her to live in such a showplace. Now that importance dimmed. Especially since the apartment seemed unbearably empty. Sterile, Dani had called it. She was right.

Barbara forced herself to listen to her messages, noting them on the pad next to the phone. Then she turned off the lights as she retreated to the bedroom. The drapes were open. Her hands on the drawcord, she paused as she stared into the darkness. A longing shot through her as she thought of that night, how she could have changed things by simply saying yes.

The view beneath her was far different from the sultry Texas night that had beckoned to a young, passionate couple. Then, the air had been thick with untold promise, unlike the crisp mountain air she now breathed. Billy had been high on life, taking her along with him. It was a ride she'd never intended to abandon, but destiny had dealt a different hand. Ah, Billy. What *did* happen to you?

Destiny, Barbara thought with irony, remembering Dani's words. Resolutely she yanked the drapes closed, shutting away the magnificent view. As though the arrogant Kenneth Gerrard could ever be part of her destiny. Ken to her Barbie? She thought not. Not in this lifetime.

BRIGHT AND EARLY Barbara sat perched in her chair at the plaintiff's table, scribbling furiously on the legal pad in front of her. Ignoring the sidelong looks from Kenneth Gerrard, she was back in form. Adrenaline raced through her veins at the scent of battle. Deciding after a restless night that he was simply using a tactic, albeit an effective one, to distract her, she'd armed herself with resolve. And she refused to give in to his captivating smile.

Dani kept glancing at her in trepidation, then in grudging admiration, awarding her a thumbs-up for effectively dislodging one of Gerrard's better potential jurors without using one of her own strikes.

The day wore on. At the lunch break Barbara and Dani slipped away before the approaching Gerrard could reach them. Congratulating herself on the move, Barbara affected the same maneuver on her return to the courtroom, neatly cutting off any communication he might have intended. But at the end of the day she wasn't quite so lucky. Turning from a conversation with her client, Barbara found herself staring into those stunning moss green eyes.

"Miss Callister, if I didn't know better I'd think you were avoiding me."

She smiled coolly. "Perhaps your first guess was right."

His smile remained even; if anything, it grew a notch. "How about that drink? I'm still a stranger in a strange land."

She opened her mouth to refuse when she met his eyes. There was something there, something she couldn't explain. But she was drawn to him, feeling her normal reserve fade as his gaze pulled her closer. She knew she shouldn't associate with him outside the courtroom—it violated the ethics she held in high regard, ones she'd never before considered compromising. Still she found herself agreeing. "Perhaps one drink." Then she rushed on with an explanation she wasn't sure was for his benefit or hers. "I'd be heartless if I let you try to navigate the weird Utah liquor laws alone. It takes a membership in a private club to get a drink." Her eyes finally met his again and she had that same feeling of being lost in their depths. Her voice skipped a note as her breath shortened. "And I happen to have a membership."

If he was surprised at her turnaround he didn't show it. "Great." His smile broadened. "I can't think of a better guide."

Plastering on a smile that she hoped hid the sudden quivering assaulting her insides, she walked with him through the marble halls of the courthouse, her heels clicking against the slick surface.

His gaze traveled down to her seductively high heels. "You wear those ankle breakers every day?"

She flushed unexpectedly while his eyes remained steady, appraising her long legs. "You always say whatever pops into your head?"

"Most of the time." His smile deepened, that irrepressible dent in his cheek coming to life.

She sucked in the unexpected feeling that smile caused, making her think of another time. Her memory nagged at her, but instead of concentrating, she tried instead to remember that this could only be a simple drink. Nothing more. "We can walk to the Hilton. There's a club on top with a great view of the city."

Kenneth gestured to the unmatchable scenery. "From what I can see, there's a great view from everywhere here except the basements."

Ignoring the magnificent backdrop of snow-capped mountains, she slanted a glance at him. "What were you doing in a basement?"

"Research," he replied briefly, confidently.

Wishing she could dismiss his impressive reputation, she managed an equally confident smile. "Luckily I devoted my time to research *before* the trial."

His smile matched hers. "I never stop digging."

Deciding it would be easier to spar with a think tank group captain, she settled for increasing the pace, annoyed when his long legs effortlessly matched hers.

As they walked, she watched her city through his observant eyes. His gaze took in the passing scenery of tree-lined streets filled with rich architecture, a mix of buildings steeped in history, complementing those that had been built to beckon the future.

Too soon they reached the Hilton, walked through the lobby and reached a bank of elevators that could take them to the Club at the Top. They stepped into the elevator and watched as the doors began to slide closed. Suddenly a middle-aged man stuck his shoulder in the elevator opening, causing the doors to bounce open again. He entered breathlessly, pulling his laughing wife in behind him.

"Hi, folks!" the man greeted them as he placed a plump arm around his wife's waist. "Salt Lake's a great place, isn't it?" he asked with all the enthusiasm of a tourist out on the town.

Barbara nodded politely, but Kenneth demurred. "Haven't seen much of the city yet."

The man looked knowingly at his wife and then they both grinned at Kenneth and Barbara. "If you haven't seen the sights that means you've been locked up in the hotel. Yep, you two must be newlyweds. Brings back a lot of great memories."

Barbara nearly choked on the laughter bubbling in her throat. Now that was a classic misunderstanding. Glancing at Kenneth she was surprised to see an indiscernible, almost haunted expression cross his face before his smile eased into place. It tugged at something deep inside, but she was distracted as the doors whooshed open at the club level.

"Good luck to you both," the man offered before the doors shut again.

Kenneth acknowledged the comment with a curt nod, guiding Barbara into the club. Once seated, they both looked out at the incredible view as sunset swamped the sky, rendering a purple-and-blush-colored palette that contrasted dramatically with the crimson border blending into the towering mountains. It was a sight that never failed to move her. Yet now she was drawn more to the man seated across from her. One whose eyes hadn't left her face for a moment. Even when the drinks came.

He didn't make her nervous. It was something else.

A sensation she couldn't define. The same one that had drawn her to momentarily disregard the most important case of her career. Some would argue that a civil suit that involved corporate issues, rather than criminal ones, was not a matter of life or death. But gaining success in a law firm told a different story. And this win could cinch her success.

With a little finesse perhaps she'd discover what he'd been digging for in the courthouse records.

But he surprised her again. "Isn't this place a little stuffy for you?"

"How do you know I'm not in my element?" she returned, glancing around at the sedate crowd. It was a good place to bring clients. While it lacked a lot of style, it was a safe, dependable place.

An inexplicable twinkle brightened his expression. "Why don't we go somewhere else and find out?"

Dropping a bill on the table, he swept her out of the club before she could protest, leaving their drinks barely touched. Merging into the crowd that pressed into the elevator, they were soon on ground level and headed for the exterior doors when it occurred to Barbara that she hadn't agreed.

But then they were back on the sidewalk, the blush of dusk coloring the sweet-smelling air. When they passed a growing crowd on a street that had been roped off, he brightened perceptibly.

Kenneth leaned over to a young man who held a clipboard in his hand, someone presumably connected to the commotion filling the street. "What's going on?"

The bearded, long-haired youth glanced at them

from beneath little round glasses. "It's a shoot. For *Halloween VII.*"

"A movie shoot?" Barbara echoed, knowing how many movies were filmed in Salt Lake, yet not expecting to stumble into the middle of a production.

The young man glanced at his clipboard. "Yep. And we need lots of extras." He looked dubiously at their clothing, ending his perusal with Kenneth. "Real *GQ,* man. But I'm desperate, could be a great contrast. You two interested?"

Barbara was shaking her head, but Kenneth grabbed her hand and pulled her forward. Stunned by the contact, the familiar thrill that raced through her at his touch, Barbara didn't protest until she saw that she was in direct view of the cameras. "Oh, no. I didn't work off the better part of my anatomy becoming one of the most respected attorneys in town to be seen in some *horror* show!"

His gaze dropped appreciatively to that exact part of her anatomy as he ignored the rest of her protest. "And when was the last time you shed that veneer, Miss Callister?" His voice turned mockingly persuasive. "Think of the boost it'll give your image. Being on film, lots of exposure."

"I *am* thinking of my image," she muttered, while breathing in the growing feel of the crowd.

Excitement pumped through the air, a combination of the unexpected and the youthfulness of those participating. Glancing around, Barbara realized they were the only ones there not under thirty. But Kenneth didn't seem to mind, instead pulling her closer to the center of the action.

Surprisingly she felt a lift. It had been forever since

she'd let herself be drawn into the moment just for the fun of it.

"Okay, I need a couple kissing in this scene. Some of those extras." The director pivoted, his gaze coming to rest on Kenneth and Barbara. "You two. Perfect. No one would expect you. Not in those getups."

Before Barbara could think or react, Kenneth pulled her close, fitting his lips to hers, devouring her in a kiss that was in no way just for show. His mustache tickled her skin, his breath stole hers. Broad shouldered, his muscular chest met the feeble resistance of her silk blouse. Gasping for air, for sanity, Barbara couldn't resist the assault of his mouth on hers as though it hungered for more than she could give.

"Cut! *Cut!*"

The shout finally penetrated their fogged senses. Breaking apart, both of them looked into the disgusted face of the director who stood with hands on hips before tossing his arms skyward.

"That was just great. But you could have waited till we started filming!"

Barbara wished suddenly for special effects to make her disappear as the crowd around them erupted in uncontrollable laughter. The giggles traveled like a lightweight cloak, brushing aside the intensity of their kiss. Reluctantly she met Kenneth's eyes, saw the grin lurking there and surrendered to the laughter coating the night, realizing it had been too long. Far too long since she'd let herself do something so silly. Once it had been the better part of her personality; now it was a rarity.

Then it struck her. Caught up in matching wits,

then lips, she had played right into his hands. Catching his eye, she saw his smile broaden knowingly. And vowed to knock that cocky grin into the next century.

"You may have made me forget my principles for one night, Gerrard, but it ends right here." Spotting a taxi across the street, she waved her arm to signal the cabbie and briskly walked away from the roped-off area.

Kenneth strolled easily beside her, his smile deepening, those unique eyes of his seeming to swallow her. "Oh, but you're wrong, Counselor. I've just begun."

Before she could protest, he swept them both into the taxi, leaning toward the driver in a friendly manner. "We're looking for someplace different." Kenneth gestured at the Hilton across the street. "Nothing like the Club at the Top. Got any suggestions?"

The driver, a youngish man whose T-shirt read Sundance U.S. Film Festival, flashed a wide grin. "You got it." Accelerating rapidly, the taxi wove through the still-busy streets. Within a short time he pulled to a stop in front of an old, but well-maintained building. The marquee advertised a variety of touring rock groups and Barbara was surprised to recognize one from her college days.

"Look, I don't have time—" Barbara began, but Kenneth cut her off as he thanked the driver.

"This looks great, just what I had in mind." He gestured to the man's T-shirt. "You work at the film festival?"

"No, man. Just lucky enough to drive around the

famous when they get here. The festival's here every January—it's Robert Redford's big deal.''

Kenneth handed the driver the fare plus a generous tip.

The driver's smile broadened. ''Hope you two like the club.''

Kenneth answered him with a jaunty wave. ''It's got to be an improvement on where we've been.''

Barbara scowled at him, yet she didn't want to make a scene in front of the driver. Her habits as an attorney were too deeply ingrained and they included always maintaining her sense of decorum.

Kenneth closed the car door and pulled her next to him, shattering that very decorum as he reached up to pull the pins from her hair. He slipped them into his jacket pocket, then eyed her outfit with a critical gaze.

Self-consciously she straightened her shoulders. ''Something wrong?''

He cocked his head and appraised her until she felt a warm flush building in her cheeks.

''What?'' she asked in exasperation.

He reached over to the neat bow tied at the neck of her blouse. ''If this thing could just go.''

She glanced down at her tasteful, but conservative blouse. Unconsciously her hands rose to that same bit of material. ''I don't know what you mean.''

Without asking her permission, he untied the bow and tucked the material into the bodice of her blouse, creating slim-lined lapels. ''Better.''

Glancing down, Barbara saw that he'd also created a vee for her cleavage. Swallowing, she considered just how prudish it would look to return the material back to its bow.

Not giving her time to decide, he tugged her toward the door, paid the cover charge and then pulled her inside. "Look, Kenneth, I never agreed—"

A wild burst of music cut off her words. The throbbing of the drums rocked the room, set the rhythm for the other musicians in the group. It was a wild, hot sound, one that had her body yearning to sway to the beat. As though sensing her desire, Kenneth held out his hand in invitation.

The music beckoned, as did the exciting man who stood beside her. Maybe just one dance....

Sound swirled around them, enveloping them, beguiling them. It was just supposed to be a dance, she reminded herself as Kenneth's hands drifted toward her waist. Their hips rotated to the same beat, their eyes connected and Barbara could believe for a moment that their blood sang to the same pulse.

When that song ended, another began, one that told of Bogey and Bacall, of a love that couldn't end. Another lifetime ago, the song had been hers and Billy's. Now, instead, her hand was in Kenneth's as he pulled her close to sway to the softer song.

Mesmerized, she met his eyes. "This was a very special song to me," she confessed.

A shadow crossed his features, then he drew her close again.

It seemed as though she'd traveled a galaxy away from her normal life. Known as Calculating Callister, she didn't allow much time for frivolity, still less for mind-numbing music that made her want to bend into a handsome man's arms. Even if that handsome man was opposing counsel.

Like a bucket of cold water, the thought struck her, roused her from the spell he'd spun. What was she thinking? Every moral fiber of her being throbbed with the realization that what she was doing was wrong. Very wrong.

Shakily she pulled away from Kenneth and wove her way through the crowd and out the door. Outside, she took a huge gulp of the bracing night air as she told the doorman she needed a taxi. But Kenneth was only seconds behind her.

"Something wrong, Barbara?" he asked in concern.

She turned on him with a vengeance. "You know exactly what's wrong. I can't see you outside of the courtroom. Not for drinks, or movie filming or dancing...."

Their eyes met in the charged moonlight as the taxi swooshed to the sidewalk. As she broke their gaze, Kenneth opened the door for her. Barely settled inside, she felt the pressure of his hands as they caught hers through the open window. Then he stepped away. The taxi driver accelerated, leaving Kenneth to fade into the darkness.

Barbara stared at her hands, still feeling the warmth, wondering about the tingle, trying to diffuse the corresponding wave of feeling that swamped her body. There was something about this man, something familiar yet confusing. Twisting backward, she tried to see Kenneth, but he had disappeared, leaving only a pool of questions in his wake.

Chapter Two

Barbara was ready. Kenneth wasn't going to take her by surprise again. Like a general with troops in line, battle plan drawn, she entered the courtroom and walked confidently to the plaintiff's table.

And stopped still in surprise.

A single yellow rose decorated the surface. Not the typical bloodred, but rather a color that immediately made her think of her home state of Texas. Unable to resist, she picked up the delicate, fine-stemmed flower and inhaled deeply. It smelled as sweet as it looked.

The time-honored gesture touched a chord somewhere deep inside. One that she'd put on hold for years. Resolve was quickly melting and Barbara knew she needed some quick reinforcing. Even so, she glanced at the defendant's table. Kenneth met her gaze with a wink and a jaunty wave. Part of her wanted to return the gestures; another part remembered that he was the opposition. She settled for a nod and a restrained smile. His eyebrows rose as though he'd guessed her first inclination.

Rattled, she took her place and tried to concentrate

on her notes. Instead, the words swam together as the fragrance from the flower wafted through the otherwise-stale air of the courtroom, evoking thoughts of rain-washed gardens and soft-smelling sheets. *Why did that come to mind?*

Damn the man. Did he have to play such dirty pool? Once she'd been a fool for sentimental gestures. Playing the hard-and-fast games of corporate law had dulled her ability to be affected, but now, in an instant, he'd sharpened, reawakened that response.

Suddenly she remembered the summer she was eighteen, how all those feelings had overwhelmed her, taken over her life. Since then she'd been determined not to let that happen again. But now, dealing with an emptiness she couldn't explain, some part of her longed again for those feelings.

Sneaking a glance at Kenneth, she saw that his expression wasn't mocking or knowing. Instead it was thoughtful, musing, as though perhaps he could be lost in some memories of his own.

Barbara straightened, tucking the rose a tad closer as Dani approached moments before the judge took the bench. The day's proceedings got underway and for the first time, Barbara was impatient for the day to pass.

As the hours crawled by, she became more and more restless. She needed to get away from that sharp green-eyed glance to examine her unexpected reactions.

And the judge provided the perfect opportunity.

"Miss Callister, Mr. Gerrard. We're approaching the noon hour. Due to the lengthy and unexpected briefs you both filed this morning, we will adjourn until Monday morning."

Escape on her mind, Barbara scooped papers haphazardly into her briefcase.

"Strange, you don't strike me as the kind of person who's so disorganized," Kenneth commented, cocking his head to one side as he studied her.

Willing the flush she felt mounting in her cheeks to disappear, Barbara consciously slowed her movements, aligning her papers into neat stacks before sliding them inside the leather attaché case. "Just in a hurry."

"Like a kid let out of school?" he responded with an infectious grin.

Part of her wanted to shout "Yes!" But the more responsible, ingrained part of her simply sighed. "Mr. Gerrard, I'm sure you have a good deal of work to do, as well."

"Kenneth." His lips curved as he reached out to still her hands. "Surely after last night we're on a first-name basis."

Eyes riveted on his long, tapered fingers, she sucked in her breath at his casual touch. Then shook away the thought. "A mistake. One I won't repeat."

His grin broadened. "I'm wounded. I thought we'd broken that ice rather effectively."

Thawed, melted and boiled. But she wasn't going to admit it.

"*Mr. Gerrard,* I'm sure you'll want to take advantage of our long break, so I'll—"

"You're right. I want to get started right away. What do you recommend?"

"Excuse me?"

"This is your town, Barbara. What do you suggest? Hiking? Mountain climbing? Or a lazy picnic near the lake?"

"A lot of hard work," she replied, tamping down an unexpected longing for a weekend of pure play. How long had it been since she'd indulged herself? Too long, since she couldn't remember the last time she'd thrown caution to the wind, put her work on a back burner and strictly played.

But you can't play with *him,* a merciless inner voice reminded her.

"Tsk, tsk," Kenneth replied, reaching out to cup her chin. "All work and no play makes Barbara a dull girl."

Resisting the desire to lean into his hold, she swallowed an unreasonably large lump that formed in her throat. The dimple in his cheek flashed and evoked some forgotten memory, feeling. He leaned against the table, trapping her into the small, surprisingly intimate space. At some level she was aware that the courtroom had emptied. Even Dani had deserted her, muttering something about catching some rays before they disappeared. "I'm a dedicated professional, Mr. Ger—"

"Kenneth," he insisted.

"And I don't take my cases lightly," she finished as though he hadn't interrupted.

"Strange, I don't think I said I did, either." His smile didn't diminish, but shifted to an expression she hadn't seen before. "Are you telling me that you never drop your briefs and have a good time?"

Her lips nearly twitched at the reference, but she sensed he was dangerous. In more ways than just as an adversary. Something about him told her that he wouldn't be content with just a good time. He wanted to dig beneath the surface, uncover more than she was willing to reveal to anyone.

"That's right. I guess I'm just a dull girl."

"Oh, I don't think so. Somewhere beneath that steel-belted suit and tightly pinned-up hair, I suspect there's a cyclone ready to break out." He reached up to touch her neat chignon—not a dowdy bun, but a fashionable upsweep.

Yet he made her long to pull the pins out and shake her hair free just to show him... She drew herself up. What was she thinking? She needed to show him that she wouldn't be caught unawares again, or spun under one of his nonsensical spells. That she held the ethics of her profession in high esteem, that she would never consider jeopardizing them. Still, she didn't immediately pull away as his fingers trailed over her hair.

"Mr.—"

"I thought we'd settled that."

Exasperated, she managed to move away. "All right. I'll call you Kenneth, if you'll keep your hands to yourself."

His grin tipped upward, demonstrating his amusement. "You don't enjoy it?"

She guessed her flush was deepening since she could feel the warmth in her cheeks. "Of course I don't." The lie stuck like a lump of undissolved peanut butter in her mouth.

He took his time in removing his hands, but then to her dismay he used one to pick up her briefcase.

"I'm perfectly capable of carrying that myself."

She reached for the burgundy leather case but he held it just out of reach.

"Of course you are. So am I. Want to wrestle for it?"

Glancing up, Barbara considered it, then saw the watching eyes of the court clerk who waited to lock up the room. Gritting her teeth, she forced a smile. "That would be a nice follow-up to my Oscar performance last night. You win. For now."

A satisfied grin lurked at the corners of his mouth, but he kept his comments to himself. Until they reached the street and then he took the lead. "It's this way."

Her long legs easily kept up with the pace, despite her annoyance. "What's this way?"

But he'd stopped in front of a bright red convertible. "This." Before she could react, he unlocked the trunk and deposited her briefcase and his own inside, then snapped the lid shut.

"Why'd you do that?" she demanded. Enough was enough.

He shrugged. "I figured I needed some ransom to kidnap you."

"In a minute you're going to need a lawyer of your own because I'm going to call a cop."

His head was shaking. "And be caught consorting with the enemy? What *would* your client say?"

That stopped her. "But this was your idea."

"Pity, isn't it? After you finished explaining, it would still look bad." The mischievous but victorious expression on his face made her want to throw something at him, but the only thing she had left was her purse and she wouldn't put it past him to keep that, too.

"First order of the day is to get something to eat, an early dinner," he announced. "And I hear that La Caille is just the place."

She could have groaned aloud. The romantic get-away was a replica of a French château, from the charming restaurant down to the bridge-covered duck pond. Hardly the place for a quick dinner.

Barbara remained steadfastly silent, determined to ignore her handsome companion as they drove out of downtown and then onto the freeway. She could have pointed out some of the sights they passed, but she chose to ignore them. If he was boorish enough to steal her briefcase, she was stubborn enough not to enjoy the ride.

In quick time he came to the nearly hidden arched entrance that was set back in the canyon. A breath-taking backdrop of snow-capped alpine mountains stretched directly beyond the entrance as though they'd been placed there exclusively as a backdrop for La Caille's impressive grounds.

She glanced at him suspiciously. "You seem to know your way around awfully well."

"I got directions," he replied cheerfully. "Pays to ask the right people." He glanced over at her, apparently seeing her skepticism. "Actually I've been wanting to visit the area for some time. I checked things out pretty thoroughly before I got here, and this was one of the places I wanted to be sure to go."

"And you've already had time to meet the 'right' people?"

"Mostly at the hotel," he admitted. "The bell captain's a wealth of information, but I've gotten the best info so far from the chef."

"The chef?" she echoed, surprised.

"I complimented him on the first incredible meal I ate in his dining room." Kenneth shrugged his shoulders. "And he didn't mind pointing out the best of his competition in the area."

Barbara wondered about a man who could turn on the charm so easily, as he pulled into the circle drive where a valet waited to take the car. Did he have enough charm to make her forget her ideals, compromise her client's interests?

Kenneth didn't head toward the restaurant, instead taking her elbow and guiding her toward the outlying grounds where peacocks strolled majestically amid exotic breeds of birds and red-topped roosters that crowed importantly. Llamas nibbled in the lush greenery close to the groundskeeper's cottage.

Genuine down to the last detail, it was easy to believe the château and its accompanying acres had been transported from France. Caught up in the beauty, Barbara allowed Kenneth to lead her toward the tranquil pond where ducks and swans lent a graceful air. Seemingly unconcerned about his Armani trousers, Kenneth dropped down on to the wooden plank of the footbridge.

It was easy to forget that less than an hour ago they'd been in downtown Salt Lake. Protected by the high walls of the canyon and the mountains towering overhead, they seemed far removed from the city.

Unconsciously, Barbara released a pent-up breath and felt some of the tension in her shoulders dissipate.

"I was wondering when you'd relax," Kenneth commented quietly.

"Sorry. Kidnapping ups my stress level."

"I don't know. From where I'm sitting, it looks like it takes some of it away."

Barbara cast her gaze around the peaceful setting, then kicked off her shoes and let her stocking feet sink into the cool grass. Disregarding the skirt of her expensive suit, she joined him. The swans didn't so much as blink at their unexpected company, instead gliding unperturbed across the water. The call of singing birds was the only sound in the muted area, protected from wayward noise by the canyon walls and nestling mountains.

Barbara watched the graceful swans. "I must be crazy, sitting here with you when you've hijacked my briefcase that holds the work I should be doing right now."

"You have to eat," he reminded her. "Why can't it be someplace like this instead of the requisite power meal? Or even worse, a TV dinner?"

She winced, knowing that's exactly what she would have chosen. Her freezer was full of the beastly little things. One thing the frozen food companies couldn't package was atmosphere. And this place fairly reeked of it. "Still high-handed of you to assume I have the time to come here."

"Why? Is someone waiting for you?"

An unreadable expression had crossed his face as he asked the question. If asked to name it, Barbara would have guessed it was apprehension. But that couldn't be it. She moved restlessly. "Not really, but that's—"

"No boyfriend?"

She shook her head.

"Fiancé?"

"No. However—"

"And you can't be married, since your name's Callister."

She looked up sharply. "How do you know that's my maiden name?"

He smiled disarmingly. "Good guess. Actually, I was still fishing and you fell for the bait."

Her own smile was cocky. "Careful, or that rod might pull you into the water along with whatever you catch."

"Forewarned is forearmed." He stood up easily and reached his hand out for her. "And since we're too close to water for comfort, I think it's about time we feed you."

"Me?"

"You get cranky when you're not fed, I can tell. Threatening to push perfectly nice men into the water—"

"Perfectly nice men don't kidnap ladies."

He drew closer to her, his face inches from hers, the tick in his jaw pulsing, the heat from his body flowing toward hers. "And ladies know when to give in gracefully."

Her heart thumped erratically and Barbara tried to find solid ground, but all she could feel was shifting sand. Sand that threatened to suck her in, bury her.

Laughing shakily, she broke away, knowing she had to put some distance between them. "Maybe you're right. I think I do need food."

TWO HOURS LATER, after a leisurely meal that even Barbara had to admit was beyond compare, they pulled up in front of her apartment building. She knew she had to regroup. And to admit to herself that she was using a flimsy excuse to spend time with Kenneth Gerrard. She also knew she couldn't continue doing so without sacrificing her ethics.

Purposely putting on an overly bright smile, she turned to Ken. "Kidnapping's complete. Now the mission's over."

"Not quite." Moving with a grace she would have admired if it didn't mean that he'd taken her by surprise again, Ken exited the car and stood next to her door in seconds. "You've really got to decide what we're going to do."

"About what?"

"No playing dumb. It's ladies' choice. I'm all yours. Hiking, touring.... You name it."

Quickly she got out of the car. "I'm naming it. Dinner was...nice. But now I've got to get to work. My briefcase please."

But he was already shaking his head. "I'm surprised at you, Counselor. You didn't negotiate for its return, and from your reputation as a hard hitter I expected a tougher opponent."

With a sinking feeling, Barbara realized he was serious. And he had her. "Look, Gerrard—"

"This is your first volley. Don't blow it."

She exhaled and studied the dancing devilry in his eyes. "I have no obligation to go anywhere with you."

"You'd let a stranger fend for himself all weekend? No charming lunchtime company? No one to feed the ducks with?'' He shook his head without disturbing the cunningly cut locks. ''Sounds like cruel and unusual punishment to me.''

''Look, I'm bushed. All I want to do is go inside, sink into a hot tub and soak the week away.'' It was the truth, even if it was a poor negotiating point.

''Alone?''

His husky tone sent an unwanted shiver dancing up her spine. The fact that it did had her stiffening that same spine. ''Certainly. I'm not sure what—''

He held up one hand. ''Looks like we can meet halfway. You soak tonight and tomorrow I pick you up bright and early to go hiking. I'll even provide the picnic.''

She narrowed speculative eyes. He really wasn't giving in. ''Why do you want to spend time with me? It's not as though we have a great deal in common.''

He swung back toward the driver's side, obscuring his face for a moment before opening the door. ''I wouldn't say that, Counselor. We do have a case in common to argue in court.'' Revving the engine, Kenneth smiled as the car roared to life and he sped away.

Openmouthed, she stared as he left *with her briefcase.*

Fortunately she had locked the case. Hadn't she? Oh, that portended for a calm, stress-free evening. Wondering if he would be reading all her notes, her strategies. For all the diligence of her careful climb to an important position in her firm, she'd just acted like a first-class idiot. And she'd handed all her ammo to the enemy.

KENNETH LET HIMSELF into the hotel room, struck by its sterile environment. Not that it should resemble a home, but seeing Barbara again made him long for a home. He pictured her with a happy, gurgling baby in her arms, an Irish setter at her feet, wearing a welcoming smile for the one she loved.

Releasing a gusty sigh, he knew that was an unrealistic picture. Foremost, he wasn't the one she loved. And it was clear she'd changed. She wasn't a soft, pliable girl anymore. She was a woman who knew her mind. He wondered just how rigid the barricades she'd erected had become.

It was clear she didn't recognize him. He had seen snippets of uncertainty in her eyes a few times, but nothing like the overwhelming whoosh of gut feeling that had nearly flattened him when he'd first seen her. It had taken every shred of control to grin and flirt. And she'd simply been annoyed.

It pained him to see that she seemed to be living a life that held no fun, no excitement. From what he'd discovered beforehand, he knew she was an attorney married to her career. But he thought there would be more, that she would have insisted on more. Before he left, he meant to see those tension lines dissolve while she rediscovered adventure. He just hoped the journey wouldn't kill him. Again.

BY MORNING BARBARA was pacing the floor, certain Gerrard had examined everything in her briefcase, using her gullibility to win the case. She'd thought he was attracted to her as she was to him; instead he'd just played her for a fool.

She doubted he had ever intended to go on any sort of expedition with her that day, only using that excuse as a ploy. Still, she'd dressed in T-shirt and hiking shorts and had packed a backpack. With her hair pulled back in a ponytail and a minimum of makeup, she knew she didn't resemble Calculating Callister. When the doorbell chimed, she was wondering how "Unemployed Callister" would sound.

Wiping nervous hands down her hips, she made herself remain calm as she swung open the door.

And caught her breath.

If she'd thought Kenneth Gerrard was overwhelming in a well-tailored suit, she didn't know the words to express how those hidden muscles affected her as he waltzed in, long tanned legs rippling with definition. A simple T-shirt, reading Take Me, I'm Yours, exposed impressive biceps while emphasizing that his broad shoulders weren't the product of well-crafted shoulder pads.

Mouth dry, she realized it was all him.

He reached over and tweaked her ponytail. "I like it."

Distracted, she murmured a thank-you as she closed the door. "About my briefcase—"

"I forgot to tell you. It's part of the negotiation package. No talk about briefcases all day."

She forced herself to think straight. "I realize we're very different people," she began, presenting her logic as though they still stood in a courtroom. "I'm responsible, organized—some people might say to a fault, but that's how I am. I expected to work this weekend, not waste time going on hikes and picnics. This case may not be a major career maker or breaker for you, but I'm not losing sight of what I've set out to accomplish. I'm not going to waste time trying to retrieve *my* briefcase.'' She took a deep breath. ''And I'm not accustomed to running willy-nilly without a plan.''

He leaned against the hall table, crossing his feet at his ankles, drawing her attention to his muscular calves. But his words drew her gaze back up to the lazy curve of his lips. ''We'll have to do something about that, won't we?''

While she protested, he engulfed her hand in his, grabbed her jacket and backpack, and drew her out the door and then on to the elevator. Once outside, they stepped into early-morning sunshine and Barbara spotted his car. The top was down, and though she battled the thought, it brought to mind fun, reckless times without the irksome weight of responsibility.

Despite what he'd said, she intended to get her briefcase back. Deciding her best tactic was to go along with him, she slid into the seat. So far, Kenneth had been in the driver's seat every time. Glancing over at him gripping the steering wheel, she realized he still was. Literally. But that could change.

Still, there was something about the wind tossing her hair, caressing her skin, and the beat of loud rock music as it poured from the speakers to blend into the whoosh of that wind. Within minutes she felt the years peel away. Years of being a dedicated professional, a single-minded career woman with no thought of simple fun.

In little more than half an hour they'd sped up the summit toward the east canyons. Taking the cutoff to the resort town of Park City, they bypassed the picturesque center and headed for the hiking trails.

Because it was still early spring, the wildflowers

remained uncrushed, yet the season was advancing and the weather was warm enough to hike. Mountain columbine bloomed and honeysuckle scented the air, along with the fragrance of wild loaming grass and the rich aroma of pine that stretched out as far as the timberline.

Unloading a hefty-looking backpack that she suspected contained their lunch, he tossed Barbara her jacket and her backpack, snagged his own and pocketed the keys. She stared in dismay at the still-locked trunk and Kenneth's back as he walked away.

This wasn't going according to plan. She was supposed to cleverly retrieve her briefcase, bid him goodbye and be hopping the next shuttle down the mountain. Instead, her briefcase was still in his trunk and her emotions were all caught up in muscular thighs and too-tight T-shirts.

Scrambling to catch up with him, she took one more backward look at the car and loped up the path. Within minutes she realized he seemed intent on serious hiking. It didn't take long to hit the trail. Kenneth took the lead and Barbara found herself mesmerized by the rugged silhouette she faced. Slim waist and hips flowed into muscular thighs. Briefcase, she told herself. *Work. The case. The case of her career.*

But the thought skittered away with the breeze that rippled the trees. It was difficult to think about work as she watched the play of muscles in Kenneth's legs and beneath the thin cotton of his shirt.

He turned suddenly, catching her thorough survey. Flushing, she tried to appear as though she'd been studying the flora and fauna. From the satisfied look on his face, she doubted she'd fooled him for a minute.

He consulted a map. "If we take this trail, it'll lead by the waterfall, but it's a steep climb. You game?"

She was game for anything that would distract her. Besides, her competitive spirit was kicking in. She liked winning in more places than the courtroom. "I'm not only game. I'll race you there."

Kenneth glanced back, his smile lazy. "The hike will save you a workout at the gym."

"What makes you think I work out?"

His slow, thorough gaze made his smile seem to race by comparison. "You don't stay in that kind of shape from pushing papers across a desk."

Heat built. Barbara chose to ignore it. "How about you? Racquetball? Or chasing your secretary around your desk?"

His smile grew broader. "She doesn't run that fast."

She'd asked for that one. "Now I suppose you're going to tell me that she's over sixty with blue hair and twelve grandchildren."

He laughed, a rich sound, like café au lait on a balmy Orleans night. Her senses prickled. It was a laugh meant to be shared, seductive in nature. And hauntingly familiar. "Nope. She's twenty-five, a hot-looking blonde who can have her choice of any man in the firm."

"And she chose you?"

He didn't give any ground. "I do my own choosing."

Irritation laced her words. "Do you want to head toward the waterfall or not?"

Idle amusement shaded his features. "And here I was thinking I'd just asked you the same question." But he turned, leading the way.

Soon the trail steepened as Kenneth had warned her. Barbara felt her muscles straining, knowing this was a more effective workout than the treadmill and stair stepper combined. But she was determined not to show it. So he had a hot-looking secretary? Not that it was any of her concern. But she couldn't help wondering if he was this smooth all the time. Perhaps with a stable of willing women back in San Francisco who never even considered telling him no.

Glancing up the trail at him, Barbara acknowledged that she could see why. All angles and unabashed masculinity, he was a man who probably had turned many a female heart to mush. Until lately, she'd considered her own heart immune, but she didn't want to let the unexpected wave of sentimentality that had swept over her lately lower her resistance. Just because she'd been regretting her past, she didn't intend to become a number on his no-doubt-impressive list of women.

The sound of water hitting rocks finally penetrated her senses. She could see the water tumbling over the natural outcrop from the mountainside, splashing on to the boulders below. As it relentlessly carved a groove into the rock, the water smelled as sweet as she knew it would taste.

Barbara forgot her bet to beat him to the site, shrugging off her backpack and scooping up a handful of water, anticipating that first flavorful drink. It tasted even better than she'd imagined, she thought, splashing a bit of it on her face. "I don't know why I ever convinced myself that the gym was a substitute for real hiking,'' she confessed.

Kenneth laid his own backpack on the ground. "No waterfalls at your gym?"

Barbara searched for sarcasm, found none and relaxed a fraction. "The management opted for a steam room instead."

Squatting down beside her, Kenneth filled his own broad hands with water and drank deeply, then wiped his mouth as she watched. "I guess this won't kill us."

She gestured to either side of the compact falls, where no warning signs regarding the water were in place. "Nothing's posted."

He shrugged. "Doesn't matter. It's food for the soul."

"You wouldn't be going poetic on me, would you?"

"Living in big cities, we replace old-fashioned walks with treadmills, hiking with stair climbers. It's more than exercise to come up here and take a refresher course on nature." He gazed at the towering peaks above them that dominated even the endless sky. "We think we've conquered everything with our modern technology. But the gods are still going to have the last laugh."

Barbara didn't have a ready response. He reminded her of a time when she'd constantly trotted out her social conscience, questioning everything. But climbing the corporate ladder had dulled some of those questions, shoving them aside until they'd become rusty, unused. "Are you always this philosophical?"

His laugh tripped across her senses. "Just thinking

out loud. Don't tell me these mountains haven't over-whelmed you at times?"

"Actually, I think I fell in love with them at first sight. I hadn't ever seen anything to compare with the Rockies. I stepped off the plane and I was awed—simply struck dumb by how beautiful they were." She fingered the grass at her feet, absently pulling a few blades. "I guess I don't think about the scenery much anymore."

"Too much work and not enough play?"

"Something like that." She smiled. "Actually, I've been transferred across the country three times with my firm and I've found it's not smart to get too at-tached to things."

His eyes darkened. "That include people?"

Her hands stilled. "Sometimes. I have friends here and my family back home, so I'm not Orphan of the Year. But I don't put down roots too deeply."

"Hurts too much to pull them up," he replied, his voice tight.

Searching his face, she wondered about him. Did that easy grin conceal a restlessness he regretted? A lack of deep connections? A piercing arrow of intui-tiveness told her that wasn't true. But she couldn't know that. "What about you?"

"Like you, I wanted to get ahead. I'm not pointing any fingers. You don't make partner in any decent firm without sacrifices. Like chasing down new cli-ents when you'd rather be hiking with a beautiful woman."

"I didn't know you'd given up a new client to come today."

"I wasn't giving up on this opportunity, Barbara. You *are* a very beautiful woman."

One part of her mind realized that he'd sidestepped her question, but another, stronger part was responding to his last words. Since his gaze didn't leave hers, Barbara felt the heat stain her cheeks, realizing he'd actually made her blush. Accustomed to smooth, accomplished men, she didn't think she had a blush left in her. But somehow, within a few days, he'd breached defenses most men couldn't crack in months. "Bet you say that to all of your opposition."

"Lucky I never went up against Perry Mason, then."

She grinned. "The 'female' was implied."

Quaking aspens rustled as sunshine spilled on them. "But never assumed."

His hand reached out to cup her chin and she felt a ridiculous tremble. Shocked, she realized she was leaning toward him, anticipating another kiss. Wanting another kiss. Shakily, she jerked back. "If we're going to make it to the top, we'd better get going."

Amusement flickered over his expression, and his eyes told her he read her thoughts as clearly as if she'd spoken. Yet he gathered up his backpack. "Headed for the top, are you? In everything, Barbara?"

Not rising to the bait, she shouldered her pack. "I'd hate to leave you in the dust, Gerrard."

"With you for company, I'm willing."

Before she could anticipate his next move, he reached in his backpack and pulled out a bandanna that matched his own. Then he leaned forward, tying it around her forehead, tucking in the hair that wisped around her face. It was a curiously intimate gesture, one that made her catch her breath and at the same time created a confusion she couldn't name.

Deciding she was wisest to ignore him, Barbara stepped away and headed up the path, weaving her way through the brush until the trail cleared.

Glancing back to see if he was following, she swung around just in time to see his leisurely, appreciative survey of her legs.

Two thoughts leapt forward. First, she was glad she'd acquired a decent tan on her legs. And, second, she remembered exactly how she'd watched him while he was in the lead position. Bad timing reminded her that she should have thought of that earlier and let him continue leading.

Trying to act composed, she started to turn forward again when she caught his smirk—devilishly unrepentant, blatantly open. "Look, if you think you're so smart, you can lead the way to the top."

"No, ma'am." His gaze continued to travel over her. "I'm smart enough to stay right where I am."

Fuming, she sprinted upward, knowing from her burning lungs that she was setting too grueling a pace, but the damned man unnerved her. Again.

The thought floated in her mind for a moment, but the effort to breathe made her ignore it.

What was she doing? Hiking instead of working. She should be gaining an advantage instead of dallying with Kenneth Gerrard. And she certainly shouldn't be consorting with the opposition. But still she kept climbing.

Kenneth's ready smile faded as he watched her. She had grown a lot of angles and prickly corners.

Sadly he wondered if they were a defense. Considering all the defenses he'd clung to, he understood the reasons even as he cursed them.

Barbara glanced back and he adopted the grin that came so easily to him. He'd become an expert at hiding the truth. But never had it been so cruel, so necessary.

A weight settled around his heart. Even as he wanted to open doors she'd slammed shut for too long, he wondered which would be hardest to convince. Barbara, or his own teetering feelings.

Chapter Three

Barbara stared hungrily at the lunch Kenneth was unpacking. Considering how smooth and sophisticated he was, she expected nothing less than a catered feast hidden away in that backpack. She wondered if his hotel had done the honors. She was unashamedly starving after the steep incline they'd conquered.

Anticipation made her mouth water, but when he pulled out the food from a thermal warming pack, it fell open instead.

"Corn dogs!" she exclaimed. "I haven't eaten them in years. Oh, but I love them, especially with..." Her voice trailed off as he handed her packets of mustard relish. "How did you know I like them this way?"

"Good guess." He flashed a grin. "Actually, that's how I like them, and I'm egotistical enough to think someone else might share my taste."

Someone had. But that was years ago. Barbara shook her head. Jeez, she and Billy weren't the only two people in the world to like corn dogs with mustard relish. Smiling, she bit into the corn dog, then reached for her canteen.

"No need for lukewarm water. I brought drinks." Producing cans of grape and orange soda nestled in thermal holders, he balanced one can in each hand.

"Oooh. Both are my favorites." Unaware that she looked like a child torn between chocolate and bubble gum, she finally reached for the grape drink.

Kenneth popped the top on the other can. "Good. Then you can have the purple mustache."

Her hand flew automatically to her upper lip and she saw him grin. "I haven't had a grape mustache since grade school."

"Unless you brought a mirror, you won't know if you've overcome that little problem."

She was tempted to throw something at him, but at the moment she held only her corn dog and Grape Crush and she wasn't willing to sacrifice either. Instead she took a healthy bite of corn dog.

"I'm glad you're not a nibbler," Kenneth commented as he picked up his own corn dog and dressed it with relish.

"Excuse me?" she mumbled around a mouthful.

"I like someone who enjoys their food. Most women pick at it like they're expecting to find something still crawling around in their plates."

Guiltily she glanced down at her almost demolished corn dog. "I was hungry," she replied defensively.

He laughed heartily. "I hope so. I'm packing dessert, too."

Her eyes lit up before she could conceal the gleam and she sighed. "Okay, so I'm a glutton."

His gaze drifted over her slim figure. "Not so it

shows. I figure we worked off the entire day's calories on the way up here.''

''Well, this is it for me. I don't have time for dinner because after I get my briefcase back I intend—''

''Tsk, tsk. Against the rules. Besides, our day may not be over until after dinner.''

''But—''

''And we haven't even gotten to dessert.''

She wasn't waylaid by the mention of the promised dessert. ''I can't waste this much time away—''

But he wasn't listening. Instead he reached around to the backpack, dug inside and then whipped back to face her, holding two candy bars.

''Milky Way *and* Butterfingers?'' she exclaimed, distracted. She could never decide between the two. Both were her favorites. And she seldom let herself indulge in either anymore.

''You want to split them?'' he suggested.

She was tempted. Instead she reached for the Milky Way. He might be in charge of this abduction, but she was reluctant to let him totally bulldoze her. Yet once again, his knowing grin made her suspect he'd read her thoughts.

He was smart. So smart she suspected the wheels in his mind turned at terrifying degrees of speed. It made her wary. And for some absurd reason it also made her blood skim rapidly through her body as she anticipated his next move. It had been far too long since she'd had such a worthy opponent. In business, yes. But not to share a corn dog with on the top of a mountain. And despite her resistance, she relished the exhilaration.

Munching the chocolate and caramel appreciatively, she studied Kenneth as he leaned back against a tree trunk, stretching out his long legs. While she'd expected a great many surprises from a lawyer with his reputation, corn dogs and candy bars hadn't been on her list. She *had* expected a mind like a steel trap. Granted, that was true enough. But she'd also expected barracuda tactics. Somehow, hiking and corn dogs didn't fall within those boundaries.

Still, he did have her briefcase locked in his trunk.

Hoping her face wasn't transparently telegraphing her feelings, she tried to learn more about him. "Tell me, how'd you wind up at Barrett and Barrett?" she asked lazily, as though it was of no interest.

His face made it clear he saw through her. Still, he answered easily enough. "It's a medium-size firm. Not too big that I'd be swallowed up and lost in the herd, not too small that they don't carry enough moxie to play in the power cases."

"They have a great reputation," she acknowledged. That and more. The firm's name sent shivers through any litigator facing them. "You go there right out of law school?"

"No, I clerked first."

"District court?"

He kept his grin in check. "Nope. Supreme Court."

She studied him carefully. He must mean on the state level. Clerking for a justice on the federal supreme court was a rare privilege, usually given to someone with political connections on the mega power level. "Where?"

"In D.C."

Barbara kept from choking on her candy bar with

an effort. Who did he know to get that coveted position? One every law student in the country would kill for? She fiddled with the wrapper on her candy bar. "Where'd you go to law school?"

"Harvard."

"Undergraduate?" she asked carefully.

"Harvard, as well. It seemed easier to stay put."

Right. The man had apparently aced his way through the most prestigious school in the country and he made light of the experience. She knew she was facing tough competition, but this was formidable even for her. Suddenly she was curious. She simply wanted to know more about him. "Where are you from, Gerrard?"

His brows lifted at her change of address, but he didn't comment. "Spent a lot of time on the East Coast going to school."

She wiped her hands against the grass, then hugged her knees. "Before then?"

"Beach bum mostly."

Cocking her head, she studied him. Despite his engaging grin, she suspected that he was far too intense to be content occupying his mind with only a surfboard and sand. She couldn't keep the light sarcasm from her voice. "Yeah, I hear that's how most people prepare for Harvard."

His eyes shifted and she had the uncanny feeling that he was concealing something, but his voice was even. "I didn't spend all my time at the library, either. Sure, I cracked the books to keep up my grade point average, but I didn't give up everything else."

He said that as though he thought she had, and for some reason that stung. Seeing how smoothly sophisticated he was, she easily believed that he had had a very well-rounded upbringing. But he seemed reluctant to divulge much about himself. Which made her want to learn all that more about him.

She leaned back, turning on the questions. "So, do you have someone waiting back home?"

"Not really."

"No girlfriend?"

His lips eased into a grin as he realized she was repeating his own interrogation nearly verbatim.

"Fiancée?"

"Nope."

"And since men don't change last names when they marry, I can't begin to guess if Gerrard's your maiden name."

"Touché, Counselor."

She continued without missing a beat. "Actually, I was just fishing and you fell for the bait."

He held up his hands in surrender. "You worry me, Barbara. Are you this good in court, too? Should I be sending back to the office for reinforcements?"

She shrugged. "I can keep up pretty well." She paused for effect. "Without threatening to throw opposing counsel into the nearest lake."

His grin broadened, sending a strange feeling tripping through her midsection. "It's good to see you finally making a mistake. *You* were the one who threatened to dunk *me*."

"Ah. But you're the one who needs dunking."

His eyes darkened and she felt a corresponding heat. "You could be right. But are you ready to take on the task?"

Birds sang in the stillness, reminding her of just

how isolated they were. A whisper of wind teased the aspens and pushed through the giant firs, releasing a tangy pine scent.

Feeling an unaccustomed attack of nervousness, Barbara latched on to her can of soda as she tried to feign a lack of concern. "Really, Gerrard, you're so dramatic."

He moved fast for a large man. In less time than it took to raise the can to her lips, he was at her side, his face inches from hers. She sucked in a breath and forgot to release it. She was used to men who played politely, safely. She sensed he was anything but safe. *Dangerous* came to mind.

Dangerous and determined.

Especially when his breath eased over her lips and his hands shot out to trap her against the tree. Her stare riveted on the shape of his lips, the mustache that curved over them. She remembered how his mouth had fit against hers, the electrifying reaction she'd experienced.

Suddenly afraid to repeat that mistake, she jerked away, feeling instead the imprint of his lips against the vulnerable skin of her neck. It was as though he'd guessed her move before she made it, and counter-attacked.

But the warmth of his breath against her neck unnerved her equally. Her heart beat rapidly—almost painfully—as his lips traveled over that same skin, lingering on the curve of her jaw. Then his strong hands framed her face and she was lost.

Bracketed in his touch, she sank into the embrace as his lips quested for hers. How could one touch be so gentle, yet so strong? She sensed purpose as his lips firmed over hers, then traced their outline. One of his hands kneaded the back of her neck, while the other pulled her closer.

It was an exploration, an adventure.... It was madness. Yet she let the insanity continue as she felt him absorb her taste, as she memorized his.

His tongue danced, dueled, mesmerized. Somewhere in the back of her mind she remembered that she shouldn't be doing this—not with him. For once, her body was overruling her mind. Even though tantalizing licks of memory were surfacing, ones that told her once she'd enjoyed something this special, this intense. Then her body took over again, drowning in the feel of his hands, his lips against hers.

Wanting to moan with the pleasure she sensed he could offer, she forced herself to pull back instead. Her voice was shaky as she managed an unconvincing laugh. "I see the corn dogs and chocolate have gone to our heads. You ready to head back down the mountain?"

His husky voice poured over her like aged whiskey, offering both fire and seduction, yet he met her gaze evenly. "If that's all you're game for."

Scrambling to her feet, Barbara felt an overpowering need to put distance between them. All of the confusing emotions she'd been feeling lately were ganging up on her. Despite her regret for things missing in her life, such as a soul mate and children, she was allowing her emotions to race along unchecked. She didn't know anything about this man, yet she'd allowed him to derail her normally ordered life. She had to remember her priorities. It was simply wrong to be with this man. She could be jeopardizing everything that was important to her. And right now she needed to be concentrating on her career, on this case.

As she had for far too long.

Shaking away the unwanted thought, she knew she needed to regain her solid footing. Not think about his offer that she'd refused. Even now, her body tingled with awareness, unexpected need; and a shiver skittered up her spine at the purposefulness she read in his expression.

Oh, yes. Very dangerous.

ALONE, INSIDE her own apartment at last, Barbara leaned against the closed door, letting her body sag against the solid oak. Every nerve sang with awareness, every emotion had been run up the flagpole. She didn't know when she'd felt so cornered, so exhausted, so totally intimidated.

And so alive.

Even now she could picture Kenneth Gerrard's smile, the expression in his eyes, the unmistakable purpose in his firm, muscled body. It had taken every shred of her control to resist him the rest of the afternoon. Even more to try and convince him to return her briefcase and end their forced time together.

But he'd flatly refused.

Sighing, Barbara moved away just as the doorbell pealed. Couldn't the man give it up? Didn't he realize she'd almost exhausted the remainder of her control? Not stopping to question the bisecting path of those two thoughts, she blew her bangs from her eyes.

Exasperated, she flung the door open and demanded, ''Now what?''

Dani's widened eyes revealed her surprise while

she held both hands upward in a questioning pose. "What'd I do?"

"Sorry. Bad timing."

"Glad I'm not whoever you're gunning for."

Barbara pushed a hand through her hair. "I'm not really gunning for anybody. I'm just... I guess I don't know exactly what I'm doing."

Dani wrinkled her forehead. "Now that doesn't sound like you."

"I'm kind of confused."

Dani reached out and laid one hand against Barbara's forehead. "Coming down with a fever?"

"Possibly," she muttered. "Come on in."

Dani moved inside, seeing the unexpected clutter of backpack and jacket on Barbara's sofa. Her eyebrows rose.

But Barbara didn't notice, heading instead to the kitchen. "I thought you were going to get some rays this weekend."

Trailing comfortably behind her, Dani perched on the stool opposite the snack bar. "In other words, what am I doing here?"

Barbara handed her a diet Coke. "Nope. Actually, it's nice to see a safe face."

Dani reached up automatically to touch her cheek. "Safe? Now that's not a description I've heard before."

"Nonthreatening. No ulterior motives."

"Which I take it means someone else has been hammering at you." She thought for a moment, her face suddenly opening with a dawning realization. "It's that barracuda Gerrard. Don't tell me you've been seeing him this weekend?"

Barbara spluttered for a moment.

"You *have!*" Dani squealed. "Tell me everything. Don't leave out one scintillating detail."

"Sorry to disappoint you. There aren't any *scintillating* details."

Dani's eyes narrowed. "Not from lack of trying, I suspect. So how'd this come about?"

Barbara filled her in on the briefcase-napping.

"Pretty clever man," Dani said after she heard the tale. "He gets you and the inside plan on our strategy all in one fell swoop."

"He hardly *got* me," Barbara hotly denied.

"I don't know. Looks to me like he got under your skin pretty bad."

The indignation drained out of Barbara and she sighed. "He confuses me."

"Want to tell me about it?"

"I went with him because I thought I could get my briefcase."

"Backfired, huh?"

"With a sonic boom. He still has my briefcase and...let's just say I don't need to be spending any more time with him outside of the courtroom."

"You're good, Barb. You won't compromise the case."

Barbara shrugged. "Maybe."

"Is this a chink in the famed armor? From you?"

"We all have our moments."

Dani studied her friend. "There's more to it this time. He's got you shook. This doesn't have anything to do with that sentimental streak you were feeling, does it?"

"You mean grabbing on to the first available man

because I heard my biological clock ticking?" Barbara pursed her lips and stared meaningfully, drawing out her words for emphasis. "I don't think so."

"It's funny what regret can make you do," Dani mused, ignoring Barbara's words. "People jump into marriages for no good reason, have babies they don't really want...."

"I don't think I've gone *completely* around the bend," Barbara answered dryly.

Dani shrugged. "You're a prime candidate, kid. Successful, driven and feeling your share of guilt."

"What have I got to feel guilty about?"

"Guilt, regret. Call it what you want. Part of you's wishing you had said yes to Billy's marriage proposal. And now here's another dynamic man making a play for you and it's knocking the pins out from under you. What if you say no again and there's not another chance? And what if this is the opportunity to correct that first mistake? And what if—"

"That's a lot of 'what ifs,'" Barbara inserted. "And even more imagination than fact. Let's face it. I've just been working too hard—even for me. After the weekend I'll get things back into perspective."

"I'd say the best you can hope for is to retrieve your briefcase. And how do you plan to do that *and* avoid Mr. Wonderful?"

Good question. Barbara pushed her wayward bangs from her face. Even her hair had gone wild this weekend. She gazed at her friend. "And here I thought you were the calm in the storm."

Dani grinned. "When did you ever consider me calm?"

Barbara managed a grin of her own. "I think it

might have been when you were asleep. Or possibly before you were born.''

Plopping hands on hips, Dani cocked her head as she stared at her friend. ''You look different. Younger, relaxed, more hip.''

''You suggesting I looked like Joan Crawford before?''

Dani sipped her drink, then smiled devilishly. ''Close, but no cigar.''

''Don't feel you have to mince words to spare my feelings,'' Barbara replied with more than a touch of exasperation.

''I just told you that you're looking good,'' Dani protested.

''In a roundabout way…say, via Antarctica.''

''Don't go all touchy on me. One of your best assets has been your ability to let all that mushy emotional stuff wash over you.''

Barbara paused. ''It has?''

''Sure. Everybody else gets all caught up in every minor crisis, real or imagined, and you just troop through it all, not letting it touch you. Makes you a great lawyer.''

But what kind of person did it make her?

What kind of woman?

Is that what Ken saw when he looked at her? A calculating attorney with all the emotions of a corpse? Sickened, Barbara slid down and sat on the stool opposite Dani's. When had her career become more important than anything else in her life?

''It'll be easy for you to keep everything in perspective,'' Dani commented as she picked up a banana from the bowl of fruit on the counter.

Barbara dragged her thoughts back to the present. "What do you mean?"

"You're Calculating Callister, remember?"

As though she could forget. The practical side of her had nothing to do with a silly moment of regret, nor her attraction to someone who was obviously the worst choice in men.

However, even while she was steeling herself to be practical, an errant thought tripped restlessly through her mind, reminding her that she *had* enjoyed her day with him. And despite all the reasons why she shouldn't be, she was attracted to the first man in over a decade who made her think beyond just the moment. Who made her want to dig through those forgotten feelings and retrieve them.

She turned away from her friend's questioning gaze by wandering toward the laundry room. Barbara remembered Kenneth's surprising behavior on their hike. Making her laugh over the unexpected, like corn dogs and grape soda. Making her want in a totally different way. Suddenly she wished for a mirror so she could confirm Dani's words. Did she really look younger? She certainly felt that way.

She reached up to touch her hair, her fingers colliding with the bandanna Kenneth had placed there. The material was a nubby cotton and she rubbed her knuckles over its ridgy pattern. Feeling silly, yet compelled to do so, she pulled the bandanna from her forehead and lifted it to inhale its fragrance. It still smelled of him. Closing her eyes, she could picture his smile, those eyes that beckoned to her. Almost familiar, yet...

"Earth to Barbara. Have you gone off the deep end, my friend? What's that? Your bandanna?"

Embarrassed, yet refusing to let it show, Barbara shoved the bandanna into her pocket. "It's nothing. I'm just tired and I have a million things to do still."

"On Saturday night?"

Barbara figured she might as well get it over with. "I agreed to go to dinner with him tonight."

Dani's eyebrows shot up like twin signals of disbelief. "So, are we back to playing Barbie and Ken? And can I have the dream house when you're through?"

"You're irrepressible. I'm going to dinner because he still has my briefcase. I'm not putting up with any more stalling. I get it back tonight."

"Over dinner?" Dani asked incredulously. "A little wine, a little candlelight, then you bop him over the head and retreat with the goods?"

"Exactly what I had planned," Barbara replied dryly. "Do you think I should ply him with grapes and a little hot oil body massage, too? Or do you think that would give my game away?"

Dani's eyes sparkled even as they widened. "I don't know, but I love it that you're finally playing. My, how the mighty have fallen."

Barbara rolled her eyes. "You're an impossible romantic, Dani. You should team up with Cupid and the two of you could get a monopoly on Valentine's Day."

But Dani had already tuned her out. "What are you wearing? Not that boring stuff you usually wear to work, I hope. You need something sexy and slinky—"

"I think I know how to dress for a dinner date."

"Let's go check out your closet," Dani replied, ignoring her as she stalked in that direction, leaving Barbara to trail into the bedroom after her. Waving Barbara into the shower, Dani took over clothes selection duty.

An hour later nearly every bit of clothing Barbara owned was strewn out across the bedroom and Dani was still digging in the back of the closet.

"Dani, please. It'll take me hours to put this mess back together."

"You don't have hours." Dani's voice sounded muffled, as though she were standing on her head in the back of the closet.

"No kidding." Something Barbara had been trying to point out to her friend since she'd attacked the closet.

"This is it!" Dani suddenly shrieked. "I didn't know you had it in you to buy something like this…" Her voice trailed off as she let out a low wolf whistle. "Hell, he ought to turn over the keys to his office if you show up in this."

Dani emerged, holding up by far the most provocative dress Barbara had ever owned. And never worn. With good reason— because it was so provocative. It had been an impulse buy, one a determined saleswoman had talked her into, in a moment when she'd been feeling vulnerable, but she'd never had the nerve to actually wear it.

Barbara groaned. "I can't wear that!"

"Why not?" Dani held the hanger up higher, slowly twirling the dress around, highlighting the wisp of black silk that had been designed to drive a man crazy. "I'll admit it grabs you, but it's exactly right. He won't know what hit him. You'll get your briefcase and, if you're lucky...maybe even something better."

"You're a sick woman. If I show up in that he'll...he'll..." What exactly would he do, she wondered? And why was a suddenly persistent part of her wanting to know? A half-forbidden thrill raced through her as she tentatively accepted the dress when Dani offered it.

Holding it against her body, Barbara turned slowly and looked into the mirror, remembering again why she'd given in and bought the sinfully expensive, equally outrageous dress. She'd wanted to know how a dress like this made a woman feel. Even more so, what it did to the man who saw her in it. How would it feel to discover just what kind of blood ran in Kenneth Gerrard's veins? Corporate or passionate?

It was too tempting.... Far too tempting. She started to lower the dress when she caught the expression on her own face in the mirror. She *did* look younger, more daring. And with the dress...

Not taking time to rethink her decision, she clasped the dress more firmly in her grip. Seeing Dani's startled, disbelieving expression, she grinned at her. "Don't just stand there. Start looking for jewelry, shoes...."

Dani's whoop resounded through the apartment. Barbara thought briefly of her conservative neighbors who detested noise, then discarded her concern. You're only young once, she decided.

Chapter Four

Unreasonably nervous, Barbara handed the parking valet her Jag keys. She wasn't quite sure if his whistle was for the car. Or for her.

Tugging at her abbreviated hemline, she smoothed moist hands down the sleek line of wickedly sheer black hose, then raised them to close her evening wrap. The plunging neckline was a surprise she intended only for Kenneth, not the openmouthed stares of the youngish set of parking attendants who seemed to be enjoying her entrance.

She knew that with her ebony hair, the all-black packaging was unusual. She just hadn't expected such a powerful reaction. Mustering a smile for her admirers, she escaped toward the front door. A sparkle of something bright on the pavement caught her attention and automatically she swooped down, mindful of her short skirt. It was a shiny, brand-new penny lying heads up. A sure sign of luck. All she had to do was make a wish on the penny and superstition said it would come true. Just simply wish...

Closing her eyes, for one crazy moment she let herself wish that she had said yes to Billy years ago and that she had the last fifteen years to relive with him at her side. Opening her eyes to a partial squint, she was disappointed to see that unlike the *Back to the Future* movies, no leaves were blowing from the trees, and she wasn't swirling through the fifth dimension.

Instead, time stood disgustingly still and she realized it was an impossible notion. All was normal. The boys at the curb continued smiling, their cocky grins in place, and her Jag was just now pulling into the adjacent lot.

Oh, well. At least she hadn't wasted the wish hoping for something stupid, like a better table in the restaurant, or something equally useless. Even though it hadn't worked, she tucked the lucky penny into her purse.

Managing to smile, despite her nerves, she went inside. Not relinquishing her wrap, she allowed the maitre d' to escort her to Kenneth's table. He glanced up with a ready smile, but his face went still. Watching his eyes devour her image, she gave in to a wanton, unexpected impulse. She allowed the evening wrap to fall to her elbows, giving him the entire effect of the strapless, deeply veed bodice. But it wasn't entirely lust she saw in his eyes. To her surprise, the look was laced with something else. Something that stirred her even as he rose and offered his arm.

Once seated, she took a deep breath and wondered if she could keep up the facade. Even though she felt as though she were a complete fraud, his eyes told a different story. They made her believe she had somehow stepped from her fairy godmother's pumpkin coach.

"Black becomes you," he said quietly.

"I wear it to all the best funerals," she replied, hiding her sudden nervousness under the glib words.

A light flickered in his eyes as one eyebrow rose. "Planning on burying me tonight?"

Laughing unexpectedly, she felt some of her nerves dissolve. "I'll save *that* for court."

"You want to win all the time, don't you, Barbara? It doesn't matter if you're in court—" his fingers trailed over her arm, creating a riot of sensation "—or at play."

She tried to control her uneven breathing, hoping her smile was cool. "You don't know me well enough to say that."

He smiled, the grin lifting his face, making her want to trace the laughter lines. "You Texas girls can't resist a challenge."

"What?" A frown furrowed in her brow. "How did you know I'm from Texas?"

"You can't quite hide that trace of a drawl. It's charming, but distinctive."

"And here I thought I sounded every bit like an East Coast corporate player."

He shuddered. "God, I hope not. It's one thing to act like a barracuda, it's another to sound like one."

"Now that was a backhanded insult woven into yet another insult, if I've ever heard one."

"Nope. You don't sound like a barracuda, and while you're a tough player, I don't think you'd fillet me in court without a touch of conscience."

She picked up her menu in a move designed to get her away from his touch. It was too close, too tantalizing. Despite her skimpy outfit, she felt unusually warm, nearly flushed. But a glance at Kenneth showed he remained coolly smooth as always. Yet she sensed that beneath that calm exterior lurked something else…something wilder.

"I wouldn't count on it, Gerrard." She purposely hid behind the brisk tone. It was dangerous pretending to be Cinderella. Especially when Prince Charming was smoother than frothy whipped cream.

"Hungry?" he asked.

"Sure," she agreed, knowing anything she would try to eat would stick in her throat.

"I'm not sure how they maintain their four-star status here without corn dogs and grape soda, but I imagine we'll find something palatable."

She relaxed a fraction.

Then he leaned forward, his face close to hers, destroying the calm.

Searching for the composure she normally possessed, she wondered why this particular man was able to demolish it so easily. She reached for her water glass, but his hand stopped the motion.

"Dance?"

The music was quiet classical, softly intimate. Her initial response was to refuse; then she met the challenge in his eyes and knew he was right. Texas girls couldn't refuse a dare. Rising, she walked with him to the small, secluded dance floor.

His arm circled her body and she felt an immediate reaction. For some reason his touch brought to mind endless summer nights. Shrugging away the thought, she concentrated on not sinking deeper into his embrace. But then his arms were around her, diffusing her concentration.

"What do you suppose our clients would say if they could see us now?" she asked, struggling to keep some distance.

"That a settlement's not far away."

Stiffening, she pulled back. "Don't think I'm turning to putty. Having dinner with you doesn't mean I've forgotten the ethics of my profession. I intend to fight you every inch of the way until I win."

"I expect nothing less. You're a prickly woman, Barbara Callister. Can't you just relax and forget for an evening that you're an attorney?"

She hid her face effectively against his broad shoulder while pretending to study the crowd. "Easier said than done. I've spent the better part of my life building my career. It's difficult to put that energy into neutral."

"No time for romance?"

She stumbled momentarily, then matched her steps to his. "Once. But it was a long time ago. When I was young and rather foolish."

"Young?"

"I was in college," she admitted, feeling again that strong surge of regret, wishing… Oh, wishing…

His steps faltered, then regained their natural grace. "Surely there's been someone since then."

"I *have* dated since college," she replied dryly. "But I don't give my heart quite as easily as I accept dinner invitations."

"Considering how I had to browbeat you into this dinner, I'd guess it's not an everyday occurrence."

"'Browbeat' implies you won." She glanced at him, trying to read what lurked behind his easy expression. "I'm only here because you won't return my briefcase."

"That the only reason?"

"What else?" she bluffed.

His gaze roved lazily over her alluring dress. "Nothing. But I like your change of tactics."

Blustering, she tried to protest, but the music ended and Kenneth escorted her back to the table.

She leaned across the flawless linen dinner service. "Don't think that this dress has anything to—"

The waiter arrived just then, an expectant smile hovering over his face. "Have you decided?"

Kenneth consulted her on the entrée, then placed their order.

Barbara scarcely waited until the man moved away. "All right, Gerrard—"

"Don't blow a major artery. I told you I liked the new tactics…or dress…or whatever you want to call it. You're sexy as hell in a business suit, so this is just—" he paused, as though savoring the words "—an extra added bonus. Can't I just enjoy it? With no ulterior motives perceived?"

It was difficult to argue against such a blatant compliment. She knew she should set him straight—tell him that it was a sexist comment, but secretly she was pleased with his observation.

Saved from answering by the waiter's opportune interruption, she accepted an appetizing salad. And concentrated on the tender arugula leaves rather than her distracting companion.

Continuing to be diverted throughout the main course, dessert and finally coffee, Barbara was dismayed when Kenneth suggested an after-dinner walk.

"I'm afraid not, Gerrard. This…dinner was more than I should have agreed to. No moonlight walks for me."

Surprisingly he didn't argue as he escorted her outside and down the steps. She was about to say goodnight when he flagged down a horse-drawn carriage.

"I should have known you wouldn't have been up to more walking after all that hiking today." Smoothly he handed her inside the carriage.

Barbara held her burst of anger inside, not wanting to create a scene. The driver, a pixie of a man who appeared to be in his sixties, greeted them with a tip of his jaunty felt hat as they settled in the seat. "What'll it be, folks? A fast tour of downtown, or a bit of magic?"

"The latter," Kenneth instructed him without consulting Barbara. "We spend enough time in the fast lane."

The man tipped his hat appreciatively. "I'm Sean O'Casey and it'll be my pleasure to show you this pretty little city. I've been taking newlyweds on tours for better than thirty years."

Barbara cleared her throat. "We're not newlyweds, Mr. O'Casey."

"Not yet," he replied cheerfully. "But you two got the look." With a cluck to the horse and a good deal of creaking of leather, they set off.

Startled, Barbara's gaze flew to Kenneth's before she glanced away. But she saw the fleeting gratification combined with something she couldn't quite decipher. Despite the warmth of the day, the evening was coolish. Leaning forward, Kenneth removed his jacket and draped it around her shoulders. It was like slipping into a cocoon, redolent with the scent of his cologne, and lingering warmth.

Then he took her hand. It was such a simple gesture, yet a ridiculous lump lodged in her throat as his fingers laced around hers. All the while Sean O'Casey regaled them with tales of the city's history, pointing out landmarks, driving leisurely as though the ride might last forever.

Then Kenneth began to hum. The tune was familiar, one Barbara knew well. The one they'd danced to. One that had been special so long ago.

"You said you liked this song," Kenneth reminded her.

She nodded, a lump lodged in her throat as Kenneth began a full-fledged serenade. He sang the tune she and Billy had laughed over. They had pretended *they* were Bogey and Bacall in the song, and as the lyrics had suggested, they'd dreamed of running off to Key Largo, as well. It had been part of the magic Billy had been able to create. He'd been hilarious, outrageous and one of a kind.

Then Mr. O'Casey joined Kenneth, lending his tenor to the rendition. But it was Kenneth's baritone that cut through the moonwashed night, taking her back in time. They truly had been desperately in love. Having had it all, it was easy to lose it.

Kenneth's voice drew out the words and the emotion sounded genuine, as though *he* truly missed the things they'd done. Then his eyes locked on hers as he repeated the words that claimed they could find that love once again.

Breathless, Barbara believed for that magical moment that he meant those words. But that didn't make sense. They didn't have anything to recapture.

Yet she leaned toward him and accepted the gentle kiss he offered. And for some inexplicable reason, sensed desperation in the firming pressure of his lips. The kiss deepened, growing darker, moister. She sensed danger and knew she courted it.

Doing so was totally out of character for her. As a professional, she'd become a controlled person, yet now she let those reins of control flap restlessly in the breeze that skimmed over them. And still she surrendered, her head tilting to deepen the kiss.

Kenneth accepted the nibbling of her teeth on his bottom lip, knowing she couldn't be as uncomplicated as she appeared. She'd never been before, but she'd packaged herself to seem so in control, so together.

He forgot about her control as the kiss deepened, lengthened. Her mouth was unreasonably luxurious as it heated on his. He found himself pressing against the hard, unyielding door of her emotions, wanting them to open up and spill into his hands. He wanted that facade to crack and reveal the girl hiding beneath.

Then the sounds of the night penetrated through the spell his kiss was weaving. He could sense it in the stiffening of her body, the withdrawal even before her lips left his. He damned the tourists who found their moment amusing, especially since he cared little of what anyone thought.

He resented the intrusion. But Barbara wasn't so immune to others' opinions. She scooted a short distance away on the seat as she turned her flushed face away from their onlookers. Even as he cursed the interruption, he knew he'd almost lost his own control—and control was what had kept him alive until now. He couldn't suddenly let it go.

Barbara felt the heat in her cheeks as she sneaked a glance at Kenneth. He seemed so completely unselfconscious, she was amazed. She saw amused glances from passersby, envious looks from some of the women. But none of them affected Kenneth. Who serenaded anyone anymore in this day and age? And then followed that serenade with a soul-touching kiss? And why did it make her feel so special, almost cherished?

It was an old-fashioned, sentimental gesture. She loved it, even though she was embarrassed down to her toes. She had spent so many years cultivating her professional image, not allowing for cracks in her armor. Yet in only a few days, Kenneth had undermined many of those standards.

Still, her face eased into a smile as Kenneth launched into another song with Mr. O'Casey happily accompanying him. She felt the years melting away as Kenneth made her join in a silly song that had her swaying in the carriage and clapping along to the words. Then he chose an even more active tune, requiring more body movements. It was as though he sensed her earlier discomfort.

She imagined how they must look. He, dressed in an exquisitely tailored suit, her own daring, yet classy silk confection as they jumped up and down to the antics of: *Stand up, sit down, shout, shout!*

But such fun—the kind of fun she hadn't indulged in for years. His outrageous behavior had her laughing until tears ran down her cheeks.

He paused in the song, leaning his face close to

hers as his fingers wiped away the riot of tears. "Next time I'll kiss them away."

Her heart bumped erratically in her chest, imagining another tender moment. Oh, this was going too fast! A few more evenings like this would have her believing... She didn't dare complete the thought, not with this man. The one man she couldn't become involved with. "Admittedly this has been fun, but it's getting late."

"Not going to ditch me already?" he asked, a grin starting to tug at his lips.

Feeling her own lips begin to twitch in response, she firmly clamped them shut. "I have a long day ahead of me tomorrow."

"Hmm." His tone was noncommittal. So noncommittal, it immediately made her suspicious.

"Really. I have a lot of work to catch up on."

Mr. O'Casey drew up to the spot where the ride had begun. "Once more around the city?"

"Regrettably Cinderella has to get back home." Withdrawing a generous amount of money, Kenneth slipped it into the older man's palm, then assisted Barbara out of the vehicle.

"Next time you're at the ball, give O'Casey a whistle and I'll be your driver." With a clucking sound to the horse, the old man and carriage ambled off in the darkness.

Barbara steeled herself for an argument. "Now I'm going to have to ask for my briefcase."

"Of course."

Just like that! Of course. "Then you'll give it to me tonight?"

"Oh, I didn't say that."

So the game was still on. "What are you saying?"

"That I'll give you enough clues to find it."

"Clues?" she repeated, stupefied.

"Just pretend you're on the Orient Express. With a mind like yours, you'll find it in no time."

She didn't trust the devilish expression in his eyes. "What makes you think I'll go along with this?"

"'Cause I'm a pretty lucky guy."

"Lucky?"

"Yep. It must be my rabbit's foot." He glanced downward at his well-shod feet and her gaze automatically followed his. "That's why I wear corrective shoes."

Laughter bubbled just below the surface, despite her frustration. "You're on shaky ground, Gerrard."

"I'm counting on it, Counselor."

IT HAD BEEN INSANITY to sing her the song. But since that first night, it had hovered in his mind and finally on his lips. It wasn't an explanation, not even an excuse, but Kenneth hadn't expected her to take his breath away again.

If he had any sense, his only desire would have been to rip that mind-numbing dress from her fabulous body. But it wasn't that simple. Not that his hormones hadn't kicked into overdrive. But his feelings ran deeper. He wanted to protect her, cherish her as he knew she deserved.

And now it was too late to tell her.

He'd only wanted to string this out long enough to find out who she'd become. He hadn't counted on losing his heart in the process.

But how could he tell her? How could she believe

him…and not hate him? He thought of all the angles and possibilities…and came to one inevitable conclusion. She couldn't do anything less than despise him.

He would have to concentrate on teaching her to laugh again. To live and dare. And then he'd have to walk away.

Accelerating rapidly, he steered the car through the traffic and toward the freeway, needing the feel of the speed and power beneath him. Disregarding traffic limits, he let the huge engine in the car hurl him along, riding its power, hanging curves until he reached the freeway entrance.

Then he sped into the darkness, wishing for the cover of oblivion, knowing the price he'd once paid for that oblivion. Knowing he was still paying.

AS USUAL, BARBARA ROSE early the next morning— and found a note slipped beneath her door. It contained explicit directions that directed her to a quiet, neighborhood park. At seven-thirty on a Sunday morning, the place was deserted. Following the path, as directed in the note, she came to a clearing. Tied to one of the trees was a huge bouquet of brightly colored balloons, secured with a riot of curling ribbons.

Beneath the widespread limbs of a weeping willow, a blanket was laid out. As she approached, Barbara could see that a linen tablecloth topped the blanket and it was set with bone china and sterling flatware. Yellow roses graced the center. To her amazement, crystal candle holders held long, flickering tapers.

A candlelight breakfast?

It was close to what she'd expected yesterday—but

then he'd presented corn dogs and grape soda. And now he'd surprised her yet again. As a strategist, he kept at least two steps ahead of her. It should make her uncomfortable, rob her confidence in her own legalistic ability. Instead, she felt a warm glow of admiration.

As she stared at the exquisite layout, Kenneth stepped from behind the tree, leaning one hip negligently against the trunk. "Morning, Counselor."

She caught her breath and tried to regroup. "No Egg McMuffins, Gerrard?"

His husky voice poured over her, as rich as the setting he'd created. "I wouldn't want to spoil you."

Her gaze drifted to a cart holding silver chafing dishes and an equally impressive silver coffee service. "I don't know. You could always go into catering after you lose this case."

"Still cocky, Counselor?"

"Not enough to presume that someone wants to eat breakfast in a park at the crack of dawn on Sunday morning."

She'd forgotten he could move so fast. In a few quick strides, he stood next to her, the heat from his body reaching out to touch her. Determined not to let him see how he affected her, Barbara stood her ground, lifting her chin to meet his gaze.

But he surprised her again. "More of a coffee and doughnut person, Barbara?"

"That's not—"

He stood deceptively close and she realized his words were designed to throw her off track. And he'd succeeded. Laughing shakily, she stepped away.

"Change your mind about breakfast?" he asked,

moving closer, once again closing the distance between them.

"No... That is, as long as you've gone to all this trouble..."

"No trouble, Barbara." His eyes sought her gaze and held it. "Trouble implies hesitation. And I never hesitate."

Turning back toward the cart, needing to put space between them, Barbara blindly opened the lids of the serving dishes, pretending an exaggerated interest. In a few moments, she regained her calm, feeling her breathing slow its rapid gallop through her chest. "What have you *got* in here?"

A deep laugh rumbled in his chest. "Haven't lost that healthy appetite, Counselor?"

"As you pointed out, I'm not a nibbler."

He picked up a plate and handed it to her. "Prove it."

"I haven't had the benefit of climbing a mountain this morning," she pointed out as she lifted the lid on the first dish. To her delight, blintzes filled the first dish. When she took a generous portion, he handed her a dish of fresh blueberries along with a generous dollop of sour cream. "You didn't forget anything, did you?"

His eyes darkened for a moment. "I have a remarkable memory...for details."

She tucked that bit of information away as she sat down on the blanket. It would be wise not to forget it. Many a legal case had been lost because of thoughtless inattention to detail. She didn't plan to step into that pitfall. Instead of answering, she took a bite of the tender blintze.

"This is delicious."

"I'll tell the chef you approve."

She glanced toward the outcrop of trees surrounding them. "Is he hiding out here somewhere?"

"That would hardly lend itself to the atmosphere, Barbara."

Her appreciation for the remarkable food diminished. Just what was he planning? He handed her a cup of fragrant, steaming coffee and she accepted it gratefully.

"Maybe a shot of caffeine will transport me back to reality," she commented after a sip.

"This isn't your idea of reality?"

"If you're asking if I breakfast by candlelight in the park often, I'd have to say no."

"Look what you've missed." Uncovering a small dish, he displayed succulent strawberries and raspberries dipped in thick, dark European chocolate.

Somehow she suspected it wasn't the fine meal he referred to. But she didn't want to acknowledge that. "Okay. You've succeeded in ferreting out my worst secret. Too bad you don't have a podium. And I should be standing up. But here goes anyway. My name is Barbara Callister and yes, I am a chocoholic."

"Surely that's not your worst vice?" he questioned with an exaggerated hint of disappointment.

"No, it's not. I'm known for cutting up my opposition on a daily basis."

"At least that's something I can deal with," he countered.

"We'll see, Gerrard. We'll see."

"Spoken with threat and promise." He picked up one of the giant strawberries. "I like that."

"Maybe you should be worried instead."

"Worried." He drew the word out as though testing its flavor. "No. I can think of better things to do with my time. Much better."

Barbara could, too. Like finding out what game he played. Instead she watched as he placed one of the strawberries on her plate. "Thank you."

"I could feed it to you," he offered. "But then I'm short of bamboo fans and a harem of serving girls."

"Something you'd probably enjoy far too much," she retorted, before dipping to taste the chocolate-covered fruit. The flavors exploded in her mouth and she sighed in appreciation. "These things should be illegal."

"It's the champagne," he explained. "The chef tells me he dips the fruit in bubbly first, then the chocolate coating."

It felt decadently wicked to be eating such a confection beneath the backdrop of the towering Wasatch Mountains and the green fluttering leaves of the weeping willow tree. The meal was as out of place here as this sudden burst of fun in her life.

She placed her cup back in the saucer and lowered her plate to the blanket. "Thanks for the great breakfast. But it's time to get back to reality. I've been a good sport and I'm ready to get my briefcase back."

"Remember the Orient Express," he replied, getting to his feet.

"Remember the what?"

He slanted an inscrutable glance, one that mixed well with his cocky grin. "Not the Alamo, Texas girl.'' With that he handed her an overflowing platter of sticky buns.

Trying to balance the platter without covering herself in sticky frosting, she didn't see him escape. When she looked up, he had disappeared. Baffled, she rose and searched behind the tree, expecting to see his satisfied smile. Instead she watched as a van pulled up and a small crew descended on the picnic area.

While the efficient group of men began to quickly disassemble the breakfast, a brisk-looking man who seemed dwarfed by his chef's hat and handlebar mustache approached her. ''Was the breakfast to your satisfaction, Miss Callister?''

Feeling much like Alice in Wonderland, Barbara nodded cautiously. ''And you're...?''

''Chef Timbori. I hope we'll have the pleasure of serving you again.''

Barbara cleared her throat. ''Do you do this sort of thing all the time?'' At the look of puzzlement on the man's face, she explained. ''Serve gourmet breakfasts in parks at the crack of dawn?''

Chef Timbori's face creased into a smile that eclipsed his brown button eyes. ''For certain clients, nothing is extreme.''

It didn't take much deduction to figure out that Kenneth Gerrard fit in that special category.

Chef Timbori held out an envelope.

Thanking him, she accepted it and slipped out the note. ''See you at the next stop.''

''What's he talking about?'' she wondered aloud.

The chef shrugged. ''I'm not certain, but my men will have this cleared out in a few minutes.''

Barbara thought rapidly. Remember the Orient Express. Follow the clues. He'd left some sort of clue in the breakfast display. And if she didn't find it, she couldn't retrieve her briefcase. "Wait!" she shrieked.

Startled, the chef turned and stared for a moment. "Pardon?"

"You can't take away the food and dishes yet!"

"You're still eating, Miss Callister?"

"No. I've got to go through every piece of that cart, though."

Baffled, he stared at her as though he wondered if she'd imbibed far more champagne than rested on the strawberries.

She used her most persuasive smile. "I know this doesn't make sense, but I'm looking for a clue and it's got to be in the breakfast cart or dishes. So I'm afraid I'll have to go through everything until I find it."

Chef Timbori looked as though he might be beginning to regret accepting this early-morning assignment.

And thirty minutes later, Barbara was ready to agree with him.

Every dish was uncovered, dug through, then finally emptied. Strewn around the park like the results of a miniature nuclear fallout, linen battled with china and silver serving pieces in the clearing.

And she wasn't any closer to finding the next clue.

Exasperated, she sat back on the grass and met the chef's disgusted glare. Dredging up a smile, she started to offer an apology when the bright color of the balloons waving in the light breeze caught her eye. Of course!

Without explanation, she jumped up and ran toward the tree, leaving behind an even more befuddled Chef Timbori. Searching the ribbons and the sides of the balloons, she didn't see a note. Then it hit her! Pulling a nail file from her purse, she attacked the first bright red balloon, then the pink.... In a few minutes she was surrounded by scraps of brightly colored, demolished latex...and a note telling her where to meet Kenneth next.

Exhilarated, she showed the note to the chef who waved away her offers to help clean up the mess. She sensed he wanted to be rid of her, afraid that if she stayed she'd go amuck and burst through the remaining blintzes, as well.

Humming with success, she realized she'd fallen into Kenneth Gerrard's wacky plans quite neatly. Yet...for some reason she wasn't angry.

She wasn't compromising her principles, she argued back at her conscience. She was simply cooperating so that she could retrieve her briefcase. It was a challenge, one she guessed still lay ahead...along with an even bigger one.

Chapter Five

Staring upward at the red-and-yellow-striped hot-air balloon that hovered above the expectant crowd, Barbara reconsidered her decision. First, she'd been crazy to think this wild-goose chase was fun. Second, how important was it to get her briefcase? And third, what court in the land would convict her for dismembering Kenneth Gerrard?

Then he waved to her, standing in the basket of the balloon. Tall and tanned, it was easy to spot him. It was also easy to see that he stood alone in the hot-air balloon, an unreadable expression covering his face. Other balloons filled the air, looking as though a child had released a colorful handful of festooned toys to decorate the sky.

It was a festival atmosphere, one highlighted by the perfection of the cloudless blue sky that surrounded the snowcapped mountains. Children shrieked with pleasure while they ran through the wild grass as parents watched them indulgently.

Kenneth, on the other hand was highly alert as he watched her. Barbara could sense that in the stance of his body, the unblinking scrutiny of his eyes. Then he held up a single yellow rose.

And she felt that goofy, unwanted sentimental streak taking over. What was happening to her? A moment of regret over Billy and now she was a prisoner to its effects. But she couldn't deny that regret had caused more than its share of sleepless nights. Was this unexpected chance to recapture some of the adventure of her youth another moment she would live to regret if she didn't seize it?

Her feet moved slowly at first as she wove her way toward the balloon. Then Kenneth vaulted over the side of the basket, presenting her with the rose and then helping her inside.

"This is crazy," she whispered, aware of the pilot who'd climbed inside after them.

"I know. But when was the last time you let yourself be completely crazy? Forgotten what a responsible person and attorney you are?"

Fifteen years ago. The night she'd said no to Billy.

"But—"

"Train's already leaving the station." He glanced at the ropes that supported the basket. "Or in this case, the balloon. No protests until the next stop. And the station's a long way off."

Then the balloon started rising. Barbara couldn't prevent a gasp of excitement as they soared higher, leaving the now miniature-looking crowd behind. The air was sweet, still perfumed with dew and the rich smell of firs that lined the timberline of the mountains.

It seemed natural for her to relax into Kenneth's casual hold as one of his arms looped around her waist while he pointed out the panorama unfolding beneath them. A sweep of wildflowers burst into dynamic color as the balloon crested the foothills to coast above a meadow. They dipped as though taking a whiff of their fragrance, then gained altitude.

"You've been busy, Gerrard. First the breakfast, now this. Did you give up sleeping?"

"It doesn't seem worthwhile alone."

That horse seemed to be galloping through her chest again and Barbara's heart was knocking against her ribs as though in overdrive. What was it about this man that a few simple words from him unnerved her?

Not giving her time to think that through, he leaned toward her, placing his hands on the basket rim, trapping her between his arms. This time his kiss was gentle, not demanding. It was as though he sensed the confusion raging inside her. Despite his crazy impulsiveness, Kenneth seemed to possess a timeless wisdom, one that guided him surely while she seemed adrift, captured in the spell he continued to weave.

Even though he kept his hold casual, she sensed a certain possessiveness in his touch. But as she wondered about it, Kenneth directed her attention to the ground below. Several deer grazed peacefully, undisturbed by the balloon's appearance. Then one buck lifted his head, alerted by the pilot's use of the burner, and the herd took flight. Gracefully they loped across the abundant grasses.

"I haven't been in a hot-air balloon since I've lived here," she confessed. "I didn't know what I was missing."

Something warm smoldered in Kenneth's eyes.

"We'll have to make sure you don't miss anything else."

Grateful for the pilot who occupied the basket with them, Barbara didn't answer, instead staring determinedly at the matchless scenery. She heard a low chuckle and guessed that Kenneth had read her thoughts again. Lifting the single, perfect rose blossom, she inhaled its fragrance, and blocked out every sensible thought remaining.

ONCE ON THE GROUND again, Barbara glanced back at the balloon with a touch of nostalgia. It had been a magical highlight after the extraordinary breakfast. She turned to tell Kenneth exactly that. But as she pivoted to where he'd stood, she found he'd disappeared.

"Kenneth?" she called out softly, thinking they must have been separated in the crowd. But he seemed to have absolutely vanished within seconds.

Surely he wouldn't pull the same trick twice.

But a few minutes later, not finding him, she realized he had. Searching her memory for clues from *Murder on the Orient Express,* she came up blank. It had been too long since she'd read the mystery novel. But Kenneth had mentioned stations and stops. What in the immediate vicinity could duplicate a train station?

Glancing back at the balloon, Barbara stared at the small sign that hung over the side of the basket. It read Trolley Airlifts.

Of course! Trolley Square near downtown Salt Lake. While it wasn't a train station, the trolley cars parked outside the square resembled train cars. Hoping she was right, Barbara sprinted to her car.

Barbara plunged into the traffic heading away from the balloon area, captured by the thrill of the chase. And inexplicably that had somehow become more important than recovering her briefcase.

She wondered what Kenneth had planned next. After the whirlwind day, it was hard to picture anything to top what he'd already planned. Yet she fully expected him to surprise her. She admired that in him, his ability to astonish her with quick flips of an adroit mind.

It had been an eternity since she'd been involved with someone who made her race to catch up with his thoughts...as Billy had once done. Her relationship with Billy had been a cyclone of emotion, excitement, fun and the unexpected. Perhaps that was why she had been so taken with Kenneth's methods. If this was her blasted biological clock making her respond to him, she was going to turn off the alarm.

Still she accelerated, keeping the car briskly moving toward the next destination. Train stop, she corrected herself as she turned in the parking lot.

It didn't take her long to park, but then she wandered around to the different entrances, trying to guess where Kenneth might be. Once inside, she wondered what sort of spectacular splash he had planned next.

Then she saw him, his jean-clad silhouette watchfully waiting. She felt her heart thump as it beat faster just at the sight of him. Instead of rushing toward him, she hesitated. His stance seemed like a challenge, as

though he were daring her to take those steps to reach
him.

Her pace slowed as her blood raced. Even though
he stood still, she felt as though a panther stalked her,
waiting, anticipating. The day's adventures paled next
to this moment. He seemed intense, almost reckoning.
And it occurred to her that she was seeing another
facet of him, a deeper, more urgent Kenneth, one that
was well hidden behind easy grins and fun-seeking
adventures.

His face emerged from the shadow into the stark
relief of the light pouring in from the glass ceiling.
His face was closed, strained, and Barbara felt an odd
surge of empathy for him, even though she didn't
know why. It was as though a cloud had lifted and
she saw another side of him, one that was hiding a
pain of some sort.

"Gerrard?" She hated the hesitation she heard in
her voice, but she couldn't still the cauldron of emotion that roiled within. Part of her wanted to reach
out and comfort him.... A bigger, more treacherous
part of her wanted even more.

"I knew you'd find me."

Such a simple statement, yet it spoke more strongly
than she was ready for. Still, she lifted her head and
replied recklessly, "You've come to read my mind
very well, Gerrard."

"You're a worthy opponent, Counselor." He
stepped closer, then raised a hand to sift it through
her hair.

Shivers raced through her body at the simple touch.
She suspected she'd turn to putty if he put all of his
charm into play. Forcing a shaky laugh, she stepped

back, putting some distance between them. "What do you have planned next, Gerrard? Did you rent out an entire restaurant? Or arrange to have all the roses in the flower shop delivered to our table?"

"What if it's nothing so grand?" Despite the increased space between them, she could feel the heat from his body, see the danger in his eyes. "What if I'm someone far simpler?"

"Somehow I doubt that, Gerrard." She hadn't meant to speak the words out loud. Recovering her equilibrium, she smiled at him. "But a simple ending to a complex day sounds like just what I need."

"I hoped you'd say that." However, his hold wasn't casual as he looped one arm around her shoulders. Guiding her along the mall's corridors, they walked toward the parking lot.

"We aren't staying here?" she asked in surprise.

"No, I wanted to know if you'd follow through."

It was an ambiguous statement, one she wanted to question, but they were at the door of his car. In moments, he'd pulled away from the parking lot and the downtown area. In a short time the car was climbing upward, gaining altitude quickly. It was one of the benefits of living near mountains and canyons. They were easily accessible.

She wondered which restaurant he would choose. The canyon boasted several fine restaurants with magnificent views, but he passed them by. Then he turned into a public area, deserted now in the latter part of the day. After opening the door for her, he reached in the back seat and pulled out a plain-looking picnic basket and a sturdy blanket.

"You game?"

"Always, Gerrard."

He gripped the basket more firmly, then unclenched his tight grip before walking with her to a spot that overlooked the valley. Sunset would be approaching soon and he couldn't have chosen a better place for them to view it.

As he opened the basket, she half expected sparklers to ignite. Instead, he pulled out some rather unremarkable looking sandwiches, and a bottle of zinfandel.

"No champagne, Gerrard?"

"I don't want to spoil you. Or give you a bad case of sensory overload."

She pointed to the sweeping panorama below. "What about this?"

"I can't get enough of the scenery. You people are spoiled by having it right underfoot. Most of us have to drive for miles to see anything that matches this." He handed her a sandwich and a salad.

She unwrapped the plastic, took a bite of the sandwich and immediately reassessed her opinion. It wasn't anything ordinary at all. After tasting delicately sliced smoked turkey adorned with capers, chilies, tomatoes and provolone, she knew that to call it a sandwich was an understatement. She watched as Kenneth uncorked the wine and poured them each a glass. The supper was simple, classy and again unexpected.

Though she'd never admit it to him, Kenneth Gerrard was one surprise after another.

He was quieter than he'd been since they'd met. He still had that faint reckoning look about him, making it difficult to eat despite the delicious food. Able only to finish half the sandwich, she rewrapped it in plastic, then picked up her wineglass.

"I thought you weren't a nibbler," he commented in a quiet voice.

"I'm full on adventure," she replied. "This has been quite a day for me."

"Me, too."

"You mean you don't usually wine and dine women on this grand scale?"

A ghost of his grin emerged. "You don't really expect me to divulge all my trade secrets, do you?"

Perhaps not. It might take away the magic. Startled by the thought, she leaned her face against the bracket her arms formed against her knees. "Said like a man who plays the game frequently."

A line furrowed in his forehead. "You see it as a game?"

"Having me chase a trail of clues all day is considered normal behavior?"

He laughed, a deep rumbling sound that was at odds with his contemplative mood. "And I thought you liked a challenge."

"I do!" she protested. Then realizing how ridiculous she sounded, she held out her wineglass for a refill.

Instead of filling her glass, he leaned closer, catching her off guard. His lips drifted over hers, a lazy invitation to linger. To discover.

The hand holding the glass wavered in mild protest, then she let it fall unchecked to the blanket. It seemed equally natural to lean into his hold, to fit her body to his.

The muscles she'd admired before now gripped her

with a strength that took her breath away, yet his hands were gentle as one cupped the back of her head, bringing her close. It was as though she felt quiet desperation in his touch. And a familiarity. The thought wove its way into her consciousness. It floated, nudged, then evaporated as he claimed her mouth.

His lips teased hers, then slid across her cheek to linger near the sensitive flesh of her neck. "Barbara," he breathed, with such emotion, she felt an immediate bone-melting response.

He might be leading her on, but she sensed nothing but sincerity. An almost frightening sincerity.

She felt as though she were rushing pell-mell down a river that was destined to spill over a giant waterfall. Then his lips claimed hers again and she welcomed his touch. Around them, sunset claimed the sky, sending a profusion of color nearly as great as the one exploding in her brain. The growing dusk offered solitude, as well.

Kenneth leaned her back against the blanket and Barbara felt the rough, scratchy wool, the tickle of grass against her bare legs and then his hands. Reverently they explored the line of her neck, then dipped to run over her rib cage. It wasn't an eager, brash exploration. If it had been, she could have stopped him at any time. Instead, his hands seemed intent on a journey, one that seemed predestined.

Gasping, Barbara reached up to grasp the back of his head as he lowered his mouth to her breast. It was as though her shirt and flimsy bra didn't exist. Arching off the ground toward him, she felt again that she was rushing headlong in a vehicle that traveled too fast, without benefit of steering or brakes.

In tune as he was to her thoughts, he lifted his head and placed a tender kiss on her lips. "We are in a public place, much to my regret, Barbara."

Shakily she gazed into his eyes, struck for a fleeting moment by a resemblance…something…

But he was holding out a hand to her. "It'll get cold soon, now that the sun's gone down."

Feeling at once relieved and bereft, she watched him pack up their picnic basket and blanket. Then they were in his car, speeding down the canyon and back toward town. He pulled into the parking lot behind her car, then walked her to the door.

"Last stop," he said softly, leaning forward to steal another kiss.

Her mind clouded as she sighed her acceptance and felt his lips dragging her to some deeper place where need was sharper, where want ruled the universe. His kiss was all contradictions—tender one moment, demanding the next. And she held on for the ride, letting him take her away from the impersonal place they stood, from the people they were, to a grinding passion that beat a relentless tattoo.

When he finally released her, it took a moment to readjust to reality, to remember that she stood next to her car in a parking lot. That people could walk by at any moment, and, in all likelihood, probably had.

He opened the door for her and she slid inside, not sure her legs would continue to support her. The door shut softly and he walked away. Vaguely she heard his engine rev as he waited for her to pull out. Her motions automatic, she started the car, reversed and headed out of the parking lot, seeing him disappear in the opposite direction.

She drove several blocks as though on automatic pilot, stopping for traffic lights, making the proper turns. Then it hit her. The briefcase! She'd forgotten all about it. Wrapped up in a kiss that rocked her very foundations, she'd let him slip away. The light from a neon sign shone through the window and Barbara glanced at the seat beside her. Her briefcase!

Reaching out to touch the leather portfolio and ensure that it was real, she found a ridiculous smile curling her lips. He'd said he would return the case if she followed his trail of clues, and he'd been true to his word. On impulse, she pulled into a convenience store parking lot.

Barbara reached over and picked up the briefcase, checking the locks. They remained firmly closed. Of course, she still couldn't remember if she'd locked the case. Kenneth could have examined everything and then locked her portfolio so that it looked untouched. Yet somehow she doubted he would stoop so low. She doubted he needed to.

Running her fingers over the smooth leather, she paused as she connected with something taped to the top. Carefully pulling the tape from the surface, she held the pieces of paper up to the light. Front and center tickets to the hottest show in town. A ribbon was tied around the pair of tickets along with a note in Kenneth's handwriting. ''A generous victor shares her spoils.''

It was a clever way to insinuate himself into her company again the next evening. And she couldn't quash the grin that lit her face. Still...it didn't seem right to give him an easy answer, even though she had enjoyed her excursion on his version of the Orient Express. Perhaps he should have a trail—or trial of fire—of his own to conquer first.

KENNETH SHUT THE HOTEL door behind him and sank into the club chair facing the window. He should be exhilarated. Instead he shoved one hand through his hair, disturbing the immaculate styling. Staring out the balcony, he watched the twinkle of lights that covered the valley. The towering mountains and the carpet of light somehow seemed comforting. But he was beyond comforting.

He'd started this whole thing with one intent and now it was careering out of control. He remembered the day he'd sat in his San Francisco office and opened the conflict-of-interest folder detailing prospective cases his firm intended to take on. Barbara's name on the briefs had leapt out at him. He had done everything in his power to make the case his own. He'd succeeded.

And still she didn't suspect.

Too impatient to sit, Kenneth rose and paced the generous confines of the room. The hotel was like many others he'd stayed in over the years. Places meant little to him, attachments even less. Then he thought of Barbara's face, silhouetted in the diminishing evening light, her reaction to their kiss. His own reaction.

Like a fire that had lain dormant only to be flamed to life, they'd crossed some invisible boundary. Knowing that initially he wanted only to see Barbara, to gauge what kind of life she now led, if that life made her happy, he realized his plan had now been derailed. And he didn't believe she was happy. Not in the fullest sense of the word.

Not that he discounted the value of her career, but he knew her career *was* her life. Not a complement to a well-rounded existence that included adventure, companionship...love.

Her life seemed far too sterile for that. Stiff was how she'd initially appeared. Confident, yes. But there didn't seem to be any room in her life for fun. And there didn't seem to be many times when she let down those safeguards. He suspected she hadn't lowered them in far too long.

Was this the result of something in her past? If so, how far back?

He thought of her guarded conversations, her reluctance to venture out of her well-ordered existence. She was an expert at revealing very little. But then, he'd majored in that himself. Standing at the window, he gazed over the million-dollar view, damning his choices and at the same time wondering if there had been any other road to take.

And also wondering if he could keep his own heart intact as he gave hers back.

Chapter Six

Barbara strolled into the courthouse, a kicky air in her steps. Determined to remain cool, she purposely didn't search for Kenneth. Instead, she waved to acquaintances and fellow attorneys as she moved through the hall. But everyone she waved to responded with unexpected reactions—from amazed to knowing—along with a healthy portion of winks and nods.

Shaking her head, she decided the long weekend must have had quite an effect on everyone. She navigated through the crowds and approached the courtroom her case was being tried in. Taking a deep breath, she prepared herself and opened the door.

But nothing could prepare her for what was inside.

Flowers blanketed her entire table, and the overflow of vases marched in a line around the table, as well.

Gasping, she stared at the profusion of roses, violets, daisies, peonies, asters and carnations. What in the world…?

Her gaze went from the flowers to the judge's bench. Perhaps he wasn't in yet. But that hope died as she met Judge Herbert's mottled face. And she could well guess the source of that anger. Apparently, after he'd found out about the flowers, he hadn't waited until the official start of proceedings to enter, instead lying in wait for her arrival.

"Miss Callister, I would think that an attorney of your experience would know that it is totally inappropriate to have...to have—" he spluttered, then firmed his glasses "—to have gifts of a personal nature delivered to a courtroom. In the future I suggest that you instruct your young man to use discretion and good sense. And if he doesn't have an appropriate measure of each, I expect you to inform him that such displays will cease immediately."

"But, Your Honor—"

"That will be all, Miss Callister."

"If I could approach the bench—"

Judge Herbert glared at her. "No, you may *not* approach. However, you will dispose of these flowers. Your indiscretion will force me to call a thirty-minute recess while the court is cleared."

"Sir—"

"See to it, Miss Callister." Standing up in disgust, the judge huffed his way toward his chambers.

Whirling around, Barbara caught Kenneth's smirk and saw that he was containing his laughter with a supreme effort. Dani skidded through the open doorway at that moment, her mouth agape as she took in the sight.

Barbara considered murder.

Then decided there were too many witnesses.

When she got even, it wouldn't be easily traced.

"Barbara!" Dani whispered excitedly as she

reached her side. Glancing up, over and around the table she whistled. "You must have been a *very* good girl."

"Shut up and help me move these flowers out of here. We have thirty minutes to clear the courtroom or I imagine Horrible Herbert will slap me with contempt."

Dani's eyebrows rose at Barbara's unexpected use of Judge Herbert's unofficial nickname, but she grabbed a vase.

"Could you ladies use some help?" Kenneth asked, tongue-in-cheek as he strolled up to them.

"I wondered what your next move would be, Gerrard. I didn't expect you to be quite so obvious about your sabotage." Having decided he didn't need to, and wouldn't, stoop to such measures, it was particularly hurtful to discover that he had.

"You wound me, Counselor. And you've sadly misread my motives."

"Gerrard—" she began in a voice that could be heard several rows back.

Dani punched her firmly with her elbow. "Not now, Barb. You two can take this outside later."

"Like this evening?" Kenneth suggested.

Exasperated, Barbara stared at him. "You really expect me to take you to the show tonight? I don't care if you did give me the tickets. Not after you... you..."

"What, Barbara? Sent you a room full of flowers?" He exchanged a sympathetic glance with Dani. "Hardly qualifies as a crime."

When Dani nodded in agreement, Barbara narrowed her glare and directed it at her friend.

Dani ducked her head and began gathering vases. Blossoms draped over both arms as she tried to listen while pretending to ignore the heated conversation.

"Besmirching my reputation with Judge Herbert is dirty pool, Gerrard. Granted I should have had the sense not to spend time with you outside the courtroom, but this..."

"Besmirch? Nobody talks like that anymore." He slanted his glance at Dani. "Do they?"

She started to nod her agreement, caught the fire in Barbara's eyes and opted to try and balance another vase in her arms.

"Call it what you want, Gerrard. I expected you to use your legal expertise in trying to win this case, not juvenile tricks."

"But this wasn't a legal maneuver, Barbara. It was strictly personal. I considered having the flowers delivered to your apartment, but you're never there. Since you live and breathe your work..." He let the words trail off.

Barbara felt that ridiculous thumping again. If she hadn't been forced to face Judge Herbert's wrath, she might have been knocked over by the gesture.

Strictly personal.

The words were singing their own syncopated beat in her mind.

Kenneth's smile lifted his lips. "Hey, if the judge knew what a gem you are, he'd never have gotten so upset."

Her pleasure dimmed as her eyes narrowed, thinking of other horrifying possibilities that would embarrass her in the courtroom. "What other tricks have you got up your sleeve?"

"Don't you trust me?" he asked, evoking Dani's aid with another beseeching look.

But Barbara cut off any reply Dani might have had. "Sure, Gerrard. Any more trust and I'll find myself the sole owner of the only swampland in the Grand Canyon."

"I can't believe you don't trust me." Wounded sincerity coated his words, even though he couldn't restrain a grin. "In my elementary school, on graham cracker day I was appointed crumb boy."

Dani gave a distinct giggle.

Barbara felt her own lips twitch. "If you want to help, Gerrard, grab a vase."

"Where are we going with these?" Dani asked, looking much like a flower waif.

"If anyone wants my opinion, I think they'd make a nice donation for a nursing home," Kenneth offered, picking up the largest vases. "Once you each pick your favorites."

"After my own heart," Dani muttered.

"And how do you suggest we get them there?" Barbara asked, secretly admiring the idea, totally unwilling to let him know so.

"I think a phone call to the florist ought to do it."

"And in the meantime?" she questioned, unwilling to completely relinquish her anger.

Kenneth caught her gaze with an ironical one of his own. "I think they'll hold them out front at the security desk. It's not like we're trying to foist off fertilizer."

"You think not?" Dani muttered.

"You'd rather be hauling fertilizer?" Barbara asked in disbelief.

Dani balanced all the vases she'd grabbed, looking as though she might topple over at any moment. "No. I'd just rather not be hearing a pile of manure."

EVEN THOUGH THE COURTROOM was now clear of every last bud and petal, Barbara's cheeks flamed every time she glanced at Kenneth. It was difficult to maintain any sort of concentration. She was normally not the sort of person to pay attention to what other people thought, but felt very conscious of her fellow lawyers' knowing snickers and amusement. Never having provided fodder for gossip, it was doubly uncomfortable to be in the hot seat. Grateful her client hadn't seen the debacle, she could only hope he didn't hear about it.

Under the guise of studying her opponent in a strictly legal sense, she let her eyes linger on Kenneth. And wondered. Had she let her personal attraction to him overrule her caution? And at what cost to her client, to her own strict set of standards? Had it truly been a purely romantic gesture? Or was it sabotage?

THE PLUCKING OF STRINGS, a patter of scales and the assorted bleating of the brass section blended with the excited hum of conversation as the orchestra tuned their instruments in preparation for the performance. A quick rapping on the conductor's stand and the overture began. Even so, the rustle of evening gowns coupled with the padding sound of tennis shoes from the more casually dressed patrons continued, along with the excited chatter that accompanied a good show.

Barbara still couldn't believe she'd agreed to go

with Kenneth. Not after the "flower fiasco," as her colleagues were calling it. She'd taken more ribbing over the flowers than anything she'd ever encountered in her professional career. And, of course, Kenneth had been understated all evening. She suspected he knew she was wary. And he was keeping his motives carefully under wraps.

As they moved down the aisle, he confidently found their seats. She glanced at hers before sitting down. "Couldn't find an ejector seat?"

"You're a prickly rose, Counselor. Petals like groomed velvet, but those thorns…"

"Should have thought of that before you planted a garden in the courtroom."

"I hear the ladies in the nursing home loved them," he replied, studying the program he unfolded.

A pang of guilt assaulted her, accompanied by the feeling that she hadn't considered all the angles of his gesture. It *was* romantic to have a room full of flowers practically laid at your feet. And even Judge Herbert had recovered his equilibrium when he'd returned to the courtroom and been informed of the ultimate destination of the flowers.

She cleared her throat. "I imagine they did."

Kenneth's eyes flashed to hers. He seemed to know that was as close as she would come to acknowledging the gift. Then his gaze continued drifting down over her emerald silk dress. It had been an impulsive decision once she'd reached into the closet. She'd considered wearing the practical suit she had dressed in that day, but something about a night out called for a softer look. Studiously she ignored the fact that it was also a more sensual look.

"Nice frock, Counselor."

She ran one hand over the sleek skirt. "This old thing?"

Kenneth reached over and cupped her chin. "Counselor," he began with mock surprise, "don't tell me you're flirting."

"I wouldn't begin to try and tell you anything," she retorted, but she didn't move her head away, connecting instead with the gaze that seemed to see right through her.

The overture ended, breaking the spell as the house lights dimmed and the curtain rose.

Barbara had looked forward to the play since she'd first seen the tickets. Now she dreaded having to sit through each act when she knew she'd enjoy baiting, and being baited, by Kenneth far more.

Then Kenneth's hand found hers. Strong, firm flesh encircled her fingers. Almost absently he rubbed each knuckle, finding the sensitive spot between her thumb and first finger. Then he turned her hand upside down, tracing the life lines that ran up to her wrist. A knot of unexpected heat formed in her stomach and with each move of his fingers a new tingle raced up each arm and then down her legs. She suspected that if someone yelled "Fire" right now, she would just have to sit and burn, unable to move under his spell. Of course there was the distinct possibility that she might erupt into flames anyway.

Kenneth angled his head so that he could whisper in her ear. "Great music."

"Uh-huh," she agreed, feeling the husky tickle of his breath on her neck.

He gave his full attention to her hands again and

the blaze grew stronger. Barbara tried to concentrate on the play, but nothing beyond the perimeter of their two seats penetrated her consciousness.

Kenneth leaned close again. "Incomparable scenery."

She swallowed, but the dry note in her throat wouldn't dissolve, so she settled for nodding her head in agreement instead.

Unperturbed, Kenneth leaned back in his chair. Barbara squinted first at the orchestra pit, then at the stage, trying to get a grip on her runaway emotions. Feeling like a teenager at her first drive-in movie, she knew she shouldn't be unnerved by simple hand holding.

However, its effects were anything but simple.

She wondered if every nerve ending in her body was connected to the hand he insidiously operated on. She could feel her pulse throb where his fingers brushed her wrist. The contrast of their hands brought to mind other things, other pleasures. The top of her hand was soft, his palm hard.

Kenneth's breath whispered against her neck as he murmured into her ear. "First-rate cast."

Considering that for all she knew they could have had Kermit and Miss Piggy on stage, she could only nod in agreement. His knee nudged hers and she wondered if it would be too obvious if she bolted and ran.

The thought had her withdrawing her hand and sitting upright stiffly as though she could close out those sensations. Kenneth angled an amused glance in her direction and she guessed that he'd read her thoughts again.

If he continued his uncanny perception of her, she

might be forced to throw in the towel on the case. What kind of bluff could she run in the courtroom when opposing counsel was privy to her thoughts?

Deliberately concentrating on the play rather than on Kenneth, after some time a portion of the story penetrated and she was taken by the sad tale. In a short time she felt the moisture gathering in the corners of her eyes as the heroine's poignant story got to her.

Kenneth leaned close. "You a sap for this sort of thing?"

Trying to pretend that she wasn't about to get weepy over a silly play, she ignored the gentle gibe. And when he offered his handkerchief at an appropriate moment, she accepted it, especially when he didn't tease her further.

The rest of the play passed and Barbara let herself be drawn into the story. Kenneth didn't renew his assault on her senses and she was grateful.

When the houselights came on and she and Kenneth blended into the crowd that swept outside, Barbara dabbed at the last of her tears. Catching Kenneth's eye, she expected a touch of ridicule; instead, he seemed thoughtfully guarded, picking up her hand and placing it within the warm shelter of his own. No pressure, no overtures, just a shared comfort. When the crowd in front of them stalled, he carved a path to the door.

Outside, the air was fresh and sweet, tinged by the coolness that always swept in on the evenings of a land that had once been reclaimed desert.

"I can't believe I get so stupid over things like

that," she explained lamely, hoping the end of her nose hadn't turned red with her tears.

"Hey, it's not a crime, Counselor. Sentimentality in the first degree rarely gets to court."

"First degree, huh? Was I that bad?"

His look was long, lazy and appreciative. "I wouldn't ever call you bad."

But now that they were outside, she could see the humor, try to ignore the heat flaring between them. "You might tomorrow in court."

"Is that a warning? Should I rush back to my hotel and delve through my notes for something I missed?"

She suspected he never missed anything, yet still she curved one side of her mouth upward in a knowing grin. "Privileged information, Gerrard."

"In that case, I won't lose any sleep worrying about it."

Sleep brought to mind images she didn't dare think about. Instead, she linked her arm with his. "Hungry?"

"That's a loaded question, Counselor."

She worked on ignoring him. "Fresh seafood at Market Street Grill, Southwestern at Pierpont Cafe...."

"Or room service at my hotel."

Barbara thought quickly. "We haven't tried a lot of the restaurants in town. There are—"

"Too many people in all of them," he interrupted. "I'm not planning to lock you in my room and ravish you." His smile turned wicked. "Not that the idea's not tempting."

"Actually, I have to be in court early."

"So do I, Counselor. We'll be at an equal disadvantage."

She was running out of arguments. "Maybe for just a snack. I'm not all that hungry."

"Pretending to be a nibbler now?" He tsked under his breath.

She stopped suddenly, the light from a street lamp pooling about her. "I'm not that comfortable about going to your hotel, Gerrard."

The honesty flared between them as strongly as their attraction.

She scraped the toe of her shoe against the pavement. "Despite the past few days, we're still on opposite sides of the case. I have an obligation to my client." She met his eyes and rushed on before he could protest. "And I'm aware you have the same obligation. But I can't let my personal concerns interfere with my professional ones."

His eyes simmered for a long moment, as though wanting to tell her something. She suspected it was something important, but then he offered his arm and she decided she'd imagined anything more serious.

"So, how fresh is this seafood place? From what I remember of my geography, Utah's a landlocked state. Since the fish couldn't possibly swim here, let's hope they didn't come by Pony Express."

Relieved, Barbara got back in step with him, even laughing at his dry wit. All the while hoping she could keep her resolve in place. Because it was dissolving faster than the seconds ticking away.

KENNETH QUESTIONED his sanity. Inviting her back to his hotel room? And what then? Seducing her and hoping she would forgive him when she found out he'd deceived her?

He pushed aside the draperies shrouding the window and was rewarded with that fairy dust display of lights covering the valley that he so admired. But his mind traveled beyond the sloping hills and the mountains that stood guard around the city.

To Texas. Fifteen years earlier.

He had been filled with fire and determination. And an overwhelming love for a stubborn, laughing girl who had recklessly accepted every challenge, pulled out the best in him and ultimately rejected his last desperate offer.

She hadn't known when she said no that he would disappear.

Sighing as the memories washed over him, he remembered, too, that she had been so different then. Maybe they had been *too* young, *too* filled with desperation. Their love had been the most important thing in their young lives.

It had overruled reason and practicalities. It had also never been matched. Or forgotten.

Pushing one hand through his hair, he wondered how he could have thought he could be this close to Barbara and remain unaffected. It was just supposed to be a lawsuit, one he could oversee. He'd planned to share a few laughs with Barbara, and then go back to his now-tidy life.

He wasn't sure why he hadn't revealed himself to her. Taken her into his confidence and made her swear not to reveal his secret. Not that it would have been easy to walk up to her and say, ''Hey, remember me? I used to be Billy Duncan." Not to mention that doing so could still endanger him.

Still, he could have somehow let her know. But a stubbornness had sprung up in him, wanting to make her recognize him in spite of all the physical changes. True, his long, wild blond hair was now colored a mahogany brown and sculpted in a *GQ* cut, and he was no longer a whipcord slim boy. And true, he'd traded jeans and T-shirts for Armani suits. Still, he wanted her to look inside and recognize his soul.

With a bitter laugh, he turned and gazed into the mirror that hung above the dresser. He'd expected a miracle.

Moving closer, he stared deeply at his own reflection, then reached up to pop out the green colored contacts he wore. If the eyes were a mirror to the soul, then his had irrevocable shades covering them.

He imagined her reaction if he were to confess everything now. He could envision the hurt, the betrayal. Knowing he needed to back off, not interfere with the life she'd created, he still felt a craving to continue what he'd started. To shake up her neat, complacent little life. He wanted her happy, damn it.

And he also wanted to be part of that happiness.

Knowing it was impossible didn't make him want it any less. Because if he continued this foolish route, he'd have to pull up stakes again, change what had finally become comfortable for him. He thought of his family, the anguish they'd been through, and knew he couldn't add more.

No, he couldn't tell Barbara.

Turning back to the window, he stared out at the carpet of light. And knew he couldn't leave her again. Yet.

ARRIVING EARLY, Barbara poked her head into the courtroom with a great deal of trepidation. To her relief, no flowers, balloons or other paraphernalia decorated the room.

Hearing the door creaking open, she swung around, expecting Kenneth. But it was Dani. Yawning and half-askew, but here nonetheless.

"Shouldn't you be inhaling coffee about now?" Barbara asked.

Dani looked sheepish. "I thought Brian might be here."

Barbara's eyebrows rose at the reference to the young attorney assisting Kenneth.

Slinging her oversize purse into the chair, Dani shook her head. "He had some papers I wanted to look at."

"Consorting with the enemy?" Barbara asked playfully.

Dani sucked in her breath. "Now that's rich, coming from you."

Barbara stilled her hands. Her face paled as she considered her friend's words. Was Dani right? Had she compromised her professional ethics? Swept up into Gerrard's roller coaster of adventure, had she ignored everything important to her? Was that why she'd felt the need to refuse his invitation to the hotel the previous evening? She'd sensed she was close to crossing a line. She didn't know it was so apparent to others.

Dani laid a hand on Barbara's shoulder. "Hey, don't get all bent out of shape. You've got a grip on things. I can tell that from how we're doing in court."

She met Barbara's gaze with a steady, unblinking look. "Don't you think I'd have said something if you were blowing it?"

"I'm not sure I would have paid attention," Barbara replied slowly. "I was so sure I had everything under control."

"Not even you can always be in control." Dani smiled. "And it's nice to see you thawing out. Gerrard may be on the opposite side of the legal fence, but he's drawn out things in you...." Shaking her head, Dani tried to explain. "It's like you're softer somehow, more like the rest of us mere mortals."

Barbara's eyebrows rose.

"Don't be offended. It's just that you were always so perfect that you were untouchable. That's why the flower thing was so great. You handled it, but everyone could see there were more layers to you."

Even though she felt more relaxed than she had in years, Barbara didn't think she'd undergone a Cinderella transformation. "I'm delighted everyone's so pleased by the new me, but nothing's worth compromising the client's interests." And that's what she'd risked. Lured by her attraction to Kenneth, she wondered if she would have played this differently. Been harder.

What had happened to Calculating Callister? Had she gotten so lost in Kenneth's plans that she hadn't been in top form?

The door creaked again and they both swung their heads toward the sound. It was Don Maroney, a reporter Barbara had dealt with in the past. He'd always given her a fair shake, so she usually gave him more information than other reporters.

"Glad I found you, Barbara. Any scoop you can tell me?"

Barbara's thoughts collided between personal and professional. Schooling them, she tried to decide what would benefit her client if revealed. Like many corporate cases, the actual facts in question were relatively simple. It was the interpretation the plaintiff and defendant had each taken that turned it into a complex legal debate.

Barbara's client, Pete Delight, originator of the now-famous Delightful Cookies, had sold his famous recipe and its exclusive rights to the Bakewell Corporation, once his fiercest rival. Weary of battling their underpricing methods in every market in the country, Pete expected to be happy once rid of the cookie recipe.

However, the huge corporation continued hounding him, claiming at every turn that he was violating his noncompetition clause of the buy-out agreement when he began selling "Pete's Peanut-Butter Brownies." Pete retaliated, saying that the brownies he now baked and sold were *not* the cookies in question.

But Bakewell was relentless. Pete next suspected they sent in operatives to steal his new brownie recipe. Fed up, Pete had sued. Bakewell promptly filed a countersuit accusing Pete of violating his exclusive, noncompetition contract. Pete shot back, saying they'd violated his soul, first by bullying him into selling his precious recipe, then by trying to steal every market and quash his newest product.

And since Pete and Bakewell each had the money to fight for their contentions, it had become a legal snowball, now involving two prestigious law firms and their top litigators.

All over a cookie.

Barbara tried not to think of it that way, but she knew she was hardly battling for world peace here. Yet Pete, with all the diversified interests he owned in addition to his cookie empire, was a valuable client. One the firm prized highly since he was responsible for millions in legal fees each year.

Staring at Don Maroney's expectant face, she wondered how to word a release that didn't make the case sound like children battling over the last chocolate chip.

Then she took a deep breath, knowing she was aiming a scud missile at the competition. "Frankly, Don, we've had concerns for quite some time that Bakewell has breached the boundaries of ethical business rivalry."

Don's eyes lit up. "You mean stolen corporate secrets? Like maybe the new peanut-butter brownie they've got on the market?" Every Bakewell cookie store in every mall all over the country was already promoting the tasty new item.

Barbara smiled, a knowing look that assured Don she had more in her arsenal. "I didn't say that. But quite often the evidence speaks for itself."

"You're a peach, Barbara. Anything else my editor's going to love?"

"Your article, if you do a good job."

She spoke with him for the next fifteen minutes. After he left, Dani whistled. "Nice day to declare war, Barb?"

"No, just to let our esteemed colleagues know that we mean business."

She might have temporarily lost sight of her goal. But she hadn't shed all reason.

Chapter Seven

Kenneth stood at the hallway outside Barbara's apartment, for once uncertain. She'd been so distant all day, politely refusing offers of lunch, dinner or basically any interaction beyond the official proceedings.

He wondered if she had an inkling.... Then he shook his head. He was sure he would have known. And he suspected that she would have been aimed to rip his heart out because of the deception, rather than withdraw.

The doorbell chimed, a quiet, dignified sound that matched the surroundings. The building seemed out of character for her, so stuffy and unbending.

From the initial quiet, he suspected she was looking through the peephole, debating whether or not to open the door.

Then it swung open.

"Gerrard."

"Evening, Counselor." He moved forward, forcing her to open the door wider.

"Since you're here, would you like to come in?"

"With a greeting like that, how can I resist?"

He watched as she closed the door, then clenched

her hands behind her back. She still wore the suit she'd had on that day, minus the jacket that lay discarded over the back of the sofa. The suit was a delicate linen, the color of champagne, and she'd softened it with an ivory silk blouse that was barely tucked in. She looked slightly rumpled and sexy as hell.

But there was a wariness in her eyes he hadn't seen before.

It made him wonder again if she'd found out the truth, but he didn't see any anger there. And he knew, despite any shell she'd hidden behind over the years, that if she had found out, she'd be a hell of a lot more than wary. He thought of what he'd discovered earlier that afternoon. It could be that, but it was, after all, only business.

"You going to tell me why you're acting this way?" he asked, shutting the door behind him. He saw her eyes go to the closed door, saw the momentary flare of panic, followed by acceptance.

"Perhaps you'll get the message now," she replied quietly. "I have work to do. And, as I've tried to remind you on numerous occasions, my first obligation is to my client."

Her back was to him as she walked into the kitchen, purposely ignoring him. He skirted the counter and stood in the small space she occupied, rather than taking a seat at the bar as he guessed she expected.

He leaned against the counter, dividing her already cramped space in half as he trapped her next to the refrigerator. "This have something to do with Cookiegate?"

She turned suddenly, obviously startled to see him so close and to see her space suddenly gone. She seemed equally startled by his words. He could see the wariness and surprise in her eyes. "What?"

"The reporter you spilled your guts to coined the term. Appropriate, isn't it?"

Her hands fluttered, then stilled. It was clear she hadn't expected him to know about the interview, or anticipated that the reporter would come to him for his rebuttal. The article hadn't hit the papers yet, but Kenneth knew the contents. He'd had his chance to give his response.

Her voice was nervous, despite the bravado. "You're fast, Gerrard."

"I'm paid to be fast. And accurate."

It was clear she was uncomfortable being trapped in the shrinking space, but he refused to make it easy for her.

"It was only a matter of time until the case went public."

"So that's why you're acting so strangely," he mused, suddenly understanding.

Her stance was defensive. "I don't know what you're talking about."

"This case isn't life-and-death." He spoke casually, wanting her to realize that in the scheme of all things their case wasn't world shattering.

"Maybe not to you. But every one of my clients is important to me." Fire flashed in her eyes and he wondered whether she was reminding herself or him.

"Every client deserves the best representation possible. That's a given. But you'll have to admit that world peace doesn't rest on the outcome of this case.

It'll earn our respective firms a small fortune and some big egos will get to fight it out to a public audience...." He paused, catching and holding her gaze. "But the fate of cookies and brownies everywhere is relatively safe."

He saw her lips curl as they fought a smile. But, stubborn as she was, she wasn't ready to give up the fight. "I told you earlier that I don't think our fraternization—"

Unable to resist, he moved closer, loving the velvet brown of her eyes, sinking into the warmth he saw there. "You're so damn beautiful. I guess some things never change."

There was a question in her eyes. One he disregarded as he pulled her toward him. He didn't care that he should be backing off, putting the distance between them. Because all he could think about was holding her in his arms...and how she tasted. Hot, sweet and strong.

Each time he'd kissed her, he remembered how it had once been for them and wanted her to remember, as well. The desire to shake her and demand that she remember him hovered in his consciousness as their lips burned together.

He could feel the slight tremble, the vulnerability that she hid so well. Why was it that he hadn't remembered that aspect? In his memories she was always so strong, so self-sufficient. And she still was. She simply hid her other needs very well.

And he didn't want her to have to hide anymore. If she needed to lean, he wanted to be the one she turned to. The insanity of that reasoning struck him as he pressed her close.

He hadn't been there for her before and he couldn't be now. The past that had once bonded them now stood between them. It was a gap that couldn't be bridged, a dichotomy without an explanation.

Loosening the pins that held her hair, he felt it spill into his hands. Like a sweep of raw silk, it was luxurious, sumptuous...like an indulgence once it was free.

Her scent crept under his skin. God, how he remembered this, the feel of her, the smell of her. Despite her other expensive habits, her scent remained the same. The aroma of fresh apples and warm sunshine still clung to her.

Pressing her close, he willed her to remember, to recognize him. Even though he knew doing so would force him to walk away.

She accepted his embrace, then pulled her face back to stare at him. "I don't believe I've ever known anyone like you, Gerrard."

Shards of pain and disappointment hit him. He knew it was best that she didn't remember. Yet...

Her voice was shaky as she stepped out of his arms. "I know you think I'm pretty stuffy, always playing by the rules, but that's who I am." Her eyes widened, then darkened. "And this is going awfully fast for me."

Fast? To him it seemed that time stood still—the past, that was. And the present persisted in crawling by. But he could see by the troubled note in her eyes, that she was disturbed by his "rushing" her. He took a mental grip on his impatience. "What do you suggest, Counselor?"

For once she looked uncertain. It occurred to him

that she had always seemed in command of the situation. It was an admirable trait, but one that was often hard to bypass. She gestured to the sterile kitchen. "I was thinking of ordering a pizza."

"Why don't you let me do that, while you slip into something comfortable…like your sweats or jeans."

Relief flashed across her face. "I can order—"

"Give it up, Counselor. You don't have to take care of every detail yourself. What kind of pizza do you like?"

"Surprise me, Gerrard." Her expression turned impish. "You've been doing that since I met you."

How true. But instead of agonizing over what could have been, he opened his wallet and slid out a card. So she wanted to be surprised….

WHEN THE DOORBELL RANG, Kenneth insisted on answering it. "I'll get the pizza, if you'll pour the wine."

Shrugging, she turned back to the kitchen, while he whipped open the door, paying the preagreed price and adding a hefty tip.

A fantastic aroma painted the air and Barbara came out of the kitchen, sniffing, with a puzzled look on her face. "I must be starving. That pizza smells delicious."

"Mmm." Kenneth remained noncommittal. He placed the carton on the dining room table that had been set for two. In his hand he still held the carton of salad.

Watching her, Kenneth let her lift the lid on the pizza carton, enjoying the look of surprise that followed. "What in the world…?"

Satisfied, he watched as she stared in astonishment at the heart-shaped pizza, her mouth falling into an O of surprise, her eyes widening in appreciation.

Then she leaned closer, identifying the artichokes, sun-dried tomatoes and capers. "Okay, Gerrard. Come clean. You didn't get this from Domino's."

"Very perceptive." Chef Timbori was a valuable man to know. It hadn't been overly difficult to convince him to bake the pizza in the shape of a heart. Once Kenneth had convinced him that there would be no trail of clues—and no demolished food and dishes.

Her expression softened as her fingers traced the unique shape of the crust. Then she reached up and kissed his cheek, a soft, gentle, tender gesture that nearly unnerved him. He almost blurted out the truth, then pictured the hurt, the betrayal. No, he couldn't do that. But he could make her laugh.

She spoke before he had to search for any words. "Your romantic streak seems to be endless."

"You said to surprise you, Counselor."

Her eyes darkened. "And you're always doing that. I shouldn't admit it, but you're always a step ahead. If I didn't know better, I'd think you'd spent a lot of time plotting things out."

Guilt nudged him. She could never know all the nights he'd sat up, wondering how to entertain her…dazzle her…hopefully give the gift of laughter back to her. "You're giving me too much credit, Counselor. Even *I* have to devote some time to my case."

"Cocky, aren't you, Gerrard?" Spunk flashed in her eyes, replacing the thoughtful contemplation, and he was relieved.

"I'll let my record speak for itself."

"Somehow I doubt that. But right now I'm starving and the pizza looks wonderful, so I'll give you a break."

Chef Timbori had outdone himself again, Kenneth decided after polishing off two pieces of pizza and a large portion of spinach salad. And the happy glow in Barbara's eyes was worth the slight arm twisting it had taken. The chef had wanted to prepare an elaborate, gourmet meal. Pizza wasn't normally in his repertoire, but he'd given in gracefully, once assured he could put his special spin on the meal.

She sighed, an almost gusty sound. It reminded him that she had an earthy appreciation of other sensual experiences, as well. "That was the best pizza I've ever had. Although it seems sacrilegious to call a meal like that simply pizza."

He lifted an eyebrow. "I imagine the chef would agree."

"So tell me, Gerrard. How'd you find out about the newspaper article?"

"It wasn't hard. Your reporter friend came to me for my rebuttal."

A spurt of betrayal crossed her face. "I didn't think he'd do that."

So, loyalty *was* extremely important to her. He tightened his jaw. "Any reputable journalist would have done the same. An article filled with only your version of the facts might make it into the tabloids, but it shouldn't be gracing the pages of a creditable paper."

She sighed. "I suppose you're right. It's just that Don Maroney and I worked together before...."

"And so he should take your side exclusively? That wouldn't be too healthy for his career."

She leveled him with a long look. "You know, Gerrard, we'd get along a lot better if you didn't insist on being right all the time."

He considered that. "I was just trying to be logical."

She rolled her eyes. "I suppose that's a testosterone thing, too." Then she held up her hand. "But I imagine we have enough on our hands with Cookiegate. I don't think we ought to take on the war of the sexes, as well."

He found himself chuckling. Especially at the impish expression on her face. He considered how differently she had acted on the first day of the trial. In comparison, she *had* softened, relaxed. "I don't know. I think we're pretty well matched." To prove his point, he moved closer and had the satisfaction of watching her back up a step.

She clutched the take-out cartons, filling her hands with cardboard defenses. "You're not making this easy, Gerrard."

He took no prisoners. "I'm not?"

She shook her head as her eyes widened.

Moving closer, he took the cartons from her hands, putting them on the table. "How do you feel about being kidnapped again?"

The throbbing of the pulse in her throat gave her away. "What did you have in mind?"

"There's a concert at Wolf Mountain tonight."

She gestured to the papers spread out on her desk. "Well, I had planned—"

He shook his head. "Too much preparation will make you jittery."

She cocked her head at him. "Is this theory from the 'wing it, and I hope my client doesn't fry' brand of law?"

He smiled, knowing he'd won. Knowing, too, she couldn't give in easily. Even when she wanted to. "I thought you could take pity on a poor, out-of-town visitor—"

"Haven't you gotten enough mileage out of that one, Gerrard?"

"Not till it stops working," he replied truthfully, watching the play of emotions cross her face.

She glanced down at the jeans she'd changed into. A note of suspicion entered those incredible eyes of hers. "Did you have this planned all along?"

"I wasn't even sure you were going to let me in." But he couldn't keep his smile from growing. "I have to admit this *has* worked out well." He would never admit how much he'd paid for the tickets. But there was a happy scalper roaming the streets tonight.

He could see the war playing out in her expressive eyes. Eyes he had always drowned in. Anger battled with amusement.

It struck him. She was changing. And for the better.

"I should work. And I *definitely* shouldn't be seeing you, since you're the opposition. But for once you're right, Gerrard. I don't want to get burned out. And it's been a while since I've been to an outdoor rock concert."

He suspected it had been far too long. But he planned to make it up to her. Along with many of the other things he knew she missed. Even though the court trial wouldn't last forever, it was the only time he had.

CLIMBING THE HILLSIDE, Barbara breathed in the tangy smell of pine, the delicate essence of wildflowers and the sweep of uncut grass underfoot. She knew it was insanity to abandon her work once again. Most especially it was crazy to agree to another evening with Kenneth Gerrard.

Yet she slipped her hand into his and went willingly to the top of the grassy slope away from any of the people dotting the hillside. The sun was making its descent, yet they were so high in the mountains, it was only a partial display. It was something flat-landers never understood—the fact that the mountains eclipsed the full sunset. But living so high in the mountains that it seemed you could reach out and touch the sky had its benefits, as well.

The stage technicians tested the amplifiers, a far different prelude to this evening than the one they'd attended at the theater. But Barbara couldn't contain the smile that had begun when she'd agreed to come with him. How long had it been since she felt free enough to climb the mountainside to attend an outdoor rock concert?

Watching him spread out the quilt on the grass, she knew it had been too long. A fleeting thought of the work she'd left behind and the conflict she still faced surfaced. Determinedly she shook both away.

He fingered the surface of the quilt, his hands dwelling on one particular square. "This material from something special?" he asked, his voice carefully controlled.

Hearing the strain in his tone, she wondered, even as she answered him. "It was from my first college dance dress. It was the most special night of my life." Because afterward, she and Billy had made love for the first time, a sweet, aching, tender, passionate moment she'd never forgotten.

Lost in the memories, her voice grew softer. "My date accidentally spilled grape soda on the dress. He felt terrible, but we were on such a high...." She laughed, explaining, "From life, that is. With Billy I never needed more. And then, after the dance, when I knew I couldn't wear the dress again, I cut out enough to make a square in my Quilt of Life."

"Is that what you call it?" he questioned, his voice husky.

"Sounds silly and sentimental, doesn't it?" And totally out of character, she realized. But there had been a time...

"Sounds nice to me," he answered quietly.

She smiled, testing his sincerity. He was so smooth and sophisticated, she doubted he dated women who'd made quilts with their grandmothers and still held on to them. She smoothed one hand over the material. "There's a scrap from my grandmother's trousseau here, my own christening dress, my mother's best party gown—even the first pair of blue jeans we convinced my mother to buy."

"A lot of history. You're lucky."

Laughing, she dismissed the comment. "Just like any other family."

Glancing up, she caught a shaft of pain crossing his face and wondered if his own family life had been an unhappy one. He'd never discussed that part of his life. She was about to ask, but he drew her closer, tangling her legs next to his, one arm draped around her.

"It's going to get pretty cool tonight," he commented, drawing the quilt up over their legs.

She couldn't have proved it with her blood temperature. It must have been soaring up to the boiling point. "You could have chosen an indoor concert," she pointed out. "I'm sure something's going on in the Delta Center."

"And miss all this?" he asked in mock horror. "Here, you'll have the stars for a roof...."

"And damp grass for a floor," she pointed out, not unkindly.

"You going to give me grief all night?"

"Would you expect any less?" she countered.

A grin curled his lips before he angled his head, tilting it toward hers. Both their smiles dissolved under the kiss. She could feel everything more acutely as though a high-intensity switch had been clicked on inside her. There was the hard line of his body against hers, the yielding expanse of the grass beneath her. There was the heat of his lips against hers, the cool mountain air that sang around them.

She could taste, as well—the lingering flavor of the wine as their tongues tangled together. Then there was the hotter, darker flavor that was his flesh. More encompassing, yet harder to recognize, was the taste of her own passion. It overwhelmed the neat categories of her life, the tidy ideals she clung to.

Yet she didn't pull away. Even when his mouth left hers to search out other susceptible passion points. Grazing the bare, sensitive skin of her neck, the hollows at her throat, he found them. She felt the hunger in his touch, imagined how it would be when completely inflamed.

Driven by the desire to reciprocate his touch, respond to his hunger, she let her hands explore. But the contact did nothing to satisfy her, instead, it increased her hunger, fed her passion.

Technicians testing the stage lights made the surrounding lights flicker. The play of light sent the stark planes of Kenneth's face into relief. Something inside her nudged, then struggled to be heard. But his lips were descending on hers again, blotting out that niggling thought.

For a magical moment, she imagined that she had recreated a night with Billy, that she *had* been granted her wish. Then it hit her.

Billy had been a boy. Kenneth Gerrard was most definitely a man.

And he defied comparisons.

Just being with him had removed the heavy cloak of her responsibilities, lessened her need to be in control. It occurred to her that this could be an elaborate plan to undermine her ability in court. But why would a litigator of his stature and expertise need to take such measures?

And she knew she didn't imagine the heated breath that met hers, the accelerated beating of his heart pressed close to hers. And she suspected that if they weren't in such a public place, there would be further evidence of his arousal.

The warm-up band was beginning to play and people seated farther down the hill were singing along. Dusk etched the sky as lights from the ski resorts blazed trails across the mountains. Enchantment filtered from the surroundings to color their mood. And it was a collective mood. She and Kenneth weren't the only ones snuggling beneath a blanket, enjoying each other as much as they did the music.

As darkness crept over them, she began to believe. That perhaps she *did* have another chance. That she could recapture that happiness she'd once lost. Kenneth pulled her close and she let her heart thaw another fraction. Maybe it was time to trust again.

Chapter Eight

Humming, Barbara danced up the steps of the court-house. Despite the late hour that she'd arrived home the night before, her spirits were high, her energy boundless. It occurred to her, frequently, that she'd failed miserably at staying away from the opposition. But it also occurred to her that she still wanted to win. Despite her attraction to the opposition.

Because, regardless of the unexpected feelings Kenneth stirred in her, the case was important. That hadn't changed.

Reaching up, she touched the hair that brushed over her shoulders. It was the first time she'd worn her hair down to court. While getting dressed that morning, it had seemed right. She hadn't relinquished her carefully chosen power suit, but the blouse was a touch softer than usual, and she'd given up the bows for good.

Feeling lighter, most assuredly younger, she swung around the corner, not squelching the lilt in her steps.

It was the shouting that halted her.

Her client, Pete Delight, and Alexander Matthews, chairman of the Bakewell Corporation, were squared off in the hall. Pete's face was florid with anger and Alexander's rock-hard jaw was set in a threatening position.

"You always were a dishonest SOB," Alexander snarled.

"This from a man who sends in spies to steal!" Pete hollered in return.

"Gentlemen, gentlemen—" Barbara tried to intervene.

But they ignored her.

"I should have known the first minute I laid eyes on you," Alexander retorted, his voice rising to match Pete's. "You started by stealing my girl. Now you think you can walk off with Bakewell's profits. Not this time!"

"Lila was never your girl!" Mr. Delight shot back. "She was mine then. She's mine now."

"You don't know *what's* yours," Alexander countered.

Barbara listened to this ancient history with interest. It explained a lot of things—like why these men were willing to spend millions squabbling in court. Mr. Alexander had apparently once been in love with Pete Delight's wife, Lila.

"And I never should have sold you my dirty laundry, much less a fine recipe that you massacred—"

"Massacred?" Alexander roared. "This from someone who bakes cardboard brownies!"

"Only because you used up all the sawdust in the state baking your rip-offs!"

A crowd was gathering and Barbara knew the fighting would only generate bad press. But neither man wanted to listen to her reasoning.

Desperate, she knew she had to exert some control before Kenneth showed up on the scene and took over, looking like a white knight rescuing a helpless lady who couldn't control two obnoxious buffoons. It would push the pendulum of advantage in his favor.

Knowing there was little else to do, Barbara sucked in her breath, then jumped in between the men, facing her client. Surprise lined his face before his intent to push her clear surfaced. But she acted first.

Shoving her briefcase in his side, she watched him gasp with surprise as the air left his lungs. Caught off guard, he allowed her to link her arm with his and lead him away. "Normally, Mr. Delight, I don't assault my own clients, but you were about to appear on the evening news—" she steered him toward the courtroom "—in a most unfavorable light, I'm afraid. We want press, but we want it to be to our advantage, when we've timed things properly. That debacle had you looking little like lovable Mr. Delight of Delightful Cookies."

Mr. Delight cursed colorfully and explicitly.

She didn't miss a step. "At least you've got your wind back. Now, are you ready for another day in court?"

Not giving him time to answer, she swung open the door and guided him inside. A backward glance at Alexander Matthews showed the blunt red stain of anger written on his face. It was clear from the rapid conversation between Kenneth and Mr. Matthews that her opponent wasn't ready to end the argument either.

Determined to remain cool, she sat next to her fuming client, acting as though nothing amiss had happened. Making copious notes on her examination for the day, she concentrated on her performance. She couldn't let the opposition know that the encounter had bothered her—it would look as though she considered it damaging.

Which she did.

She could cheerfully choke Mr. Delight, who was proving to be anything but a delight. It always amazed her. A client, who wouldn't consider performing his own surgery after consulting a doctor, thought nothing of jumping on the legal bandwagon. And Mr. Delight, whose victory rested on showing his good character and intentions, had leapt on that wagon and nearly made the horses bolt and run.

She glanced at the defense table. Kenneth, too, was making notes and Mr. Matthews was staring straight ahead, his cheeks still ruddy with the remnants of anger, but he was silent. Kenneth glanced up, caught her eye, and she saw a brief, undistinguished flare of admiration. So, he *had* seen her intervention out in the hallway.

Pleased, she returned her own attention to her notepad. She suspected it took a lot to impress him. She just hadn't counted on breaking up a brawl to win his admiration.

The day slid by rapidly. Barbara spent the entire noon hour break closeted with her client, hoping to convince him not to engage in petty arguments with Bakewell's chairman.

When she finally emerged outside on the courtroom steps, she glanced around casually. But Kenneth wasn't anywhere in sight. Swallowing her disappointment, she tried not to look as deflated as she felt.

Dani bounced down the step behind her. ''Jeez, you

look like you lost your best friend.'' Then she halted her skipping stride as she glanced around. "I get it. Gerrard didn't stop and beg you to go out tonight."

Barbara considered righteous anger, then dismissed it. Dani was right. She'd come to expect him to be asking her out at every opportunity. A strange sense of loneliness blanketed her when she realized he must have already left without trying to see her that night. She shook away the thought. After all, she'd been single her entire life. She could certainly handle a dateless evening.

"I have big plans tonight, Dani. I need to organize my notes, clean out my briefcase, set up some files—"

Dramatically Dani flung one arm against her chest. "Be still, my heart. I just hope the rest of the jet set can keep up."

"It's just a cross I'll have to bear," Barbara replied, falling in with Dani's theatrics. "I know that Di and the gang will be jealous, but sometimes I just have to be me."

Dani grinned. "Nice to see you back in the human race, Barb. Catch you in the morning."

Barbara waved as her friend loped away. It *was* great to be feeling human. There was just one drawback. Humans could get awfully lonely.

BARBARA CONSIDERED DINNER. Without checking the kitchen, she knew her choices consisted of frozen entrées or a tuna sandwich. Neither appealed to her. Instead she made a cup of chamomile tea. Now *that* should be soothing. After brewing the tea she glanced down at it sadly. One cup on the counter seemed rather pitiful.

Get a grip, she cautioned herself. Pretty soon you'll be singing sappy golden oldies and digging out the yearbooks. Just because Kenneth Gerrard had occupied all her evenings since meeting him didn't mean she couldn't be perfectly content on her own. After all, she'd managed for years. Still, an image of his grin lurked in her mind, teased her longing.

Resolutely she carried her solitary cup of tea down the hall into the den. There was plenty of work there to keep her busy. Not to mention a desk full of papers that had been ignored for too long. She'd always prided herself on her meticulous organizational skills. Stepping into the room, she glanced at the desk and realized she couldn't make that claim anymore. The place looked ruffled and neglected.

Puttering around her den, she picked up piles of papers, then replaced them without rearranging a single page. Finally she settled in a comfortable wingback chair and tucked her feet beneath her legs, her tea forgotten as her thoughts wandered toward Kenneth again.

To distract herself, she popped a tape into the VCR, watched it play a few minutes, then ejected the tape. Flipping through the channels, she watched a few infomercials and considered ordering a machine to work on her abs, or another one to chop vegetables. Nothing held her interest more than a few seconds. Disgusted, she snapped the set off, hating to admit that she couldn't concentrate on anything. Her home should be her haven, her safe harbor. Instead, she itched for something…someone….

There were a million things she should be doing. But all she could think about was Kenneth. What was he doing tonight? Was he reinventing his strategy in the case? Was that what had taken him away tonight? Or had he simply tired of pursuing a woman who persisted in keeping him at arm's length?

It had been for the best, she told herself. She had to remember that line separating personal and professional. And she couldn't forget how important this case was, regardless of how she felt about Kenneth. Pushing him away had been the right thing to do.

Then why was she sitting here consumed by him?

She thought of the previous evening, her own floundering emotions, how she had almost agreed to a different sort of ending to the evening, then fled alone into the safety of her apartment instead. Perhaps he thought she was becoming too attached.

Was she?

The most important case of her life was coasting along, and instead of spending every waking moment concentrating on it, she was devoting the majority of her thoughts to Kenneth Gerrard. Would the partners in her firm be disappointed to learn that Calculating Callister had, quite literally, turned to mush in the opposition's hands?

The remembered moments brought a flush to her cheeks even now, the heat warming her cheeks to what she suspected was a rosy glow. It had taken every ounce of self-control she possessed to say no the previous evening. And truth be told, doing so had shredded her.

"This is ridiculous," she said aloud.

But the empty apartment seemed to echo her words back.

When had she felt so rootless, so anxious? She refused to believe that a woman wasn't complete without a man, yet there was no denying how solitary her apartment seemed.

The doorbell pealed suddenly. Unbuckling her legs, she dashed toward the door, knocking over the magazine rack and a pile of papers in the process. She ignored both.

Flinging open the door, she caught her breath at Kenneth's grin.

"Evening, Counselor. I was hoping I'd catch you home."

She schooled herself not to fidget and give away her eagerness. Casually she smiled and leaned against the doorjamb, disguising her breathlessness. "Actually, I was just working, but—"

"I don't want to interrupt." He backed up a step. "I thought you might be free...."

Impulsively she reached out to grab his arm. "It'll wait," she explained too eagerly. "I was just thinking of opening some wine," she improvised, glad that when she *had* been meticulously organized, she'd put in a good stock of wines.

Feeling ridiculously happy that he was here in her apartment, she knew she shouldn't allow herself to become so dependent on another person, especially this man. But she realized he added another dimension to her life, one she'd only begun to sense had been missing when he'd started to fill that empty space.

Kenneth walked with her to the wine rack. Picking

up a bottle, he read the label, then offered it up for her approval.

Nodding her agreement, she handed him a cork-screw and found herself staring at the strength in his hands as he expertly pulled the cork, wondering how those hands would feel on her body. Weakening as she remembered how close they'd come the previous evening before she'd put on the brakes. Wishing she hadn't applied those brakes, now as she stood close to him, feeling the unresolved sizzle in the air.

Ridiculous, she reminded herself, even though she didn't move her gaze away, instead handing him two delicate goblets, seeing the desire in his eyes—wondering if that same desire was mirrored in her own.

Deep burgundy liquid filled the glasses and she tipped hers back, emptying it quickly in her nervousness.

Kenneth's eyebrows winged upward in question, but he didn't comment as he refilled her glass. The warmth of the wine replaced the anxiety in her stomach and she found herself relaxing a fraction.

"I wondered about you tonight," she blurted out, regretting the words as soon as they were out of her mouth.

His eyes flared. Then he banked the emotion.

Relieved not to see cocky assurance in his expression, she lowered her glass and smiled. "I'd hate to think you starved to death alone."

"Or had to climb a hillside by myself?" he suggested.

Nervously she spun around, turning blindly toward the kitchen, knowing it wasn't wise to think about the previous evening, the intimacy they both craved. "I'm sure there must be something to eat in here."

But his hands reached out to trap her. "Why don't you let me take care of that?"

"Another heart-shaped pizza?" she asked, feeling the heat from his hands.

"Don't think I can come up with something as original again?"

"It's okay. I'm not keeping score." But the heart-shaped pizza *had* been too original to duplicate.

He tipped up her chin and she felt the tremors radiate from his touch. "Oh, but you should."

She tried to laugh, but the sound died away as he cupped her head and drew her close. His forehead touched hers, his chin nudged hers; then he let his lips linger over hers. It was a casual, studied and therefore lethal move.

And when he released her, Barbara held tightly on to the kitchen counter for support. But he'd already moved away. Forgotten were the reasons why she needed to separate herself from him. Instead, all she could think about were reasons to disregard that logic.

Then he whipped back around, pulling a bandanna from his pocket. "Something more original than heart-shaped pizza, huh?"

Carefully he placed the bandanna over her eyes and she found herself giggling, willingly falling under his spell, even as her senses were heightened by his touch. "Are we going to be the Lone Ranger and Tonto?"

He snorted. "Some action hero you'd have been. The Lone Ranger wouldn't have gotten very far *blindfolded*. That was a mask he was wearing."

She just giggled harder.

"Okay, we're going to sit down now," Kenneth instructed, taking her arms and guiding her into a lotus position.

"In the middle of the kitchen floor?" she questioned.

He sighed mightily. "*You're* the one who questioned my originality."

"Objection, Your Honor. Counsel was badgering the witness."

"Objection overruled. The witness acted on her own recognizance."

"Picky, picky..." she muttered.

"I don't believe the court accepts that legal lingo," he replied. "Off with your head."

"As long as the punishment fits the crime," she muttered, hearing the refrigerator door opening. She cocked her head. "What are you doing?"

"That's for me to know and you to wonder."

"You're not planning to dump ketchup on me, are you?" she asked, only half joking.

"That's juvenile. Not original. Now open your mouth."

She envisioned bugs, wriggling snakes and cold, wet, slimy things. Scooting back a bit, she shook her head and reached her hands toward the bandanna, ready to tug it off. "I don't want to."

"Objection overruled. Now open."

She opened her mouth to protest and felt the brush of his fingers, then the ripe, lush taste of strawberries. Entranced, she chewed, then sighed. "Okay...that wasn't so bad." The idea of him hand-feeding her was so sensual that she didn't dare admit more. The tingle that raced through her body had nothing to do with strawberries and everything to do with his touch.

"You're too kind," he replied dryly.

"We can't have counsel getting overconfident," she replied, savoring the lingering taste of the strawberries, the touch of his fingers as they hovered near her mouth.

"Not much chance of that," he muttered. She heard a rustling of paper. "Okay, time to open."

If it was wrapped in paper, she reasoned, it couldn't be a slimy bug. Could it? Bravely she opened her mouth about an eighth of an inch.

"A little wider." His tone was dry.

She inched her mouth open a bit more and was rewarded with a compact piece of chocolate. "Hershey's Kisses!" she announced triumphantly.

"Very good. Now how about this?"

Slightly more confident, she accepted his next offering. She chewed, thought she recognized the flavor.... "Cheerios?" she finally asked.

"You were hoping for something more exotic, I see. Hmm..."

Immediately her vision of cold, slimy things returned. "No. Cheerios are okay." She gestured widely and emphatically with her hands. "No, actually, they're good. Yes. Cheerios are good...very good."

"Give it up, Counselor. It's a good thing you're *not* on the witness stand."

She sighed. "I'm done for, aren't I?"

He clucked his tongue. "Your lack of faith is highly disappointing, Counselor."

Cocking her ear, she heard the clink of glass and thanked her stars that the ketchup bottle was plastic.

And when she opened her mouth at his request, she steeled herself for something awful.

The next sensation was completely different, but after chewing tentatively, she realized it was a pickle. Crisp and cold, the pickle was delicious, especially after the bland taste of the cereal.

"Haven't got a pastrami on rye to go with that, by any chance?" she asked.

"This is more of a taster's buffet," he replied, a trace of amusement coating his words.

It occurred to her that he had anticipated her reaction. "You're loving this, aren't you, Gerrard? I bet you were one of the boys who worked the spook house just so you could smear cold spaghetti and raw liver on all the girls."

"I was wrong," he countered. "You *do* have quite an imagination." As he talked, the sound of microwave buttons clicked, the machine hummed and then buzzed as the cycle finished.

Whatever was next, he'd warmed it up in the microwave. There wasn't much point in cooking bugs, she supposed.

"This might be a bit messy," he warned just as she opened her mouth.

Expecting something goopy and awful, she was startled by the piquant taste of warm Brie on rye toast points. "Oh, yummy," she managed to say after swallowing most of it.

"I'm glad you approve," he replied dryly.

"Oh, don't get all testy." She smoothed a hand

over her blindfold. "The Cheerios were a little bland, but they *were* a surprise."

He laughed, that husky, warmed-over sound that made her stomach turn flip-flops. "Maybe you'll like this better."

Deciding that stalling would do no good, she obediently opened her mouth. Cold was the first sensation. "Ice cream," she muttered around the mouthful. Then she tasted something else. "Häagen-Dazs Chocolate Chocolate Chip!" she yelped. "My favorite!"

After the warm Brie, the contrast of the cold ice cream sent her taste buds into a frenzy.

"I take it this meets with your approval," he commented, sounding amused.

"Not unless you hand over the rest of the carton it came in," she retorted. "Then no one gets hurt."

"What? No undying curiosity about what else I might have in your refrigerator?"

Then it hit her. How had he gotten everything into her apartment…her refrigerator? His hands had been empty when he'd arrived. And the T-shirt and jeans that hugged his form wouldn't have room to hide a sack full of food. She tore off the bandanna, ready to rip into him.

And stared at her apartment key that he held out with a grin. Once again he was a step ahead.

"But…how?"

"Friends in the right places," he replied smugly.

Friends…. The only person he knew that she knew was Dani. This *would* be the case of the century. She, the key lawyer, so taken with the opposition that she ignored her work. Her able-bodied assistant talked into handing over the apartment key. Barbara nearly groaned aloud. They might as well divulge their entire strategy right now.

"Don't blame Dani," he said, correctly guessing her thoughts. "I made it sound like we might have another flower fiasco otherwise."

"Which bodes well for our side," she muttered, thinking perhaps she ought to call in reinforcements from her firm. Male ones who weren't susceptible to Gerrard's charm.

"You obviously need more chocolate," he announced, glancing at the counter full of food. "Keeps you from getting cranky."

He unwrapped a piece of candy, gently placed one hand over her eyes, then slid a piece of chocolate between her lips.

She chewed for a moment, aware of the pressure of his touch, the waves of sensation it caused. Forgotten was the food, the way he'd gotten into her apartment. Instead, she could feel the intimate touch of his hands, her own trembling response.

"Kiss?" she guessed, hearing the thready tone in her voice, knowing she referred to more than the Hershey's chocolate.

"If you say so." Then his lips closed over hers. It was a collision, an explosion, a brilliantly engineered feat of genius.

Digging her fingers into his shoulders, she felt the strength, the purpose, the complexity of the man.

Like underwater divers gasping for air, they moved toward one another, struggling to breathe again. Each sensual move they'd just played out loomed like a blatant reminder of what they really craved.

Picking up her fingers, he kissed each one, then

took them into his mouth to suckle. She wondered if she could burst just from the wanting.

"Kisses," he murmured, adorning each knuckle with one, his voice making it clear that he wasn't referring to the chocolate variety either.

He turned her hand over, grazing the delicate skin near her wrist. "Sweet, sour...warm...never cold."

Each provocative, sensual thought that accompanied their tasting session burst into full bloom. The heat that had been building between them, the passion they'd had to keep banked, now flared.

Ignited.

Blazed out of control.

Aware of the hard lines of his body, as uncompromising as the cold tiles beneath them, she yearned toward his touch, even as she acknowledged that it was a disastrous course. How would she ever explain this to the partners in her firm? *"Sorry, lost the case because I compromised my ethical and professional obligations"?*

Then his hands drifted over her rib cage, to the valley of her waist, and she was lost. Lost to a touch that inflamed like no other. Well, perhaps one other, but that was gone forever and Kenneth was here and now.

And his touch captured her, a combination of gentleness and strength. There was no questioning or hesitation in his exploration, but rather, it was a studied course of rediscovery, each movement sure and smooth.

Then he was rising, pulling her along with him. Pressed against him, hipbones abrading hipbones, she felt the full evidence of his arousal, the answering cradling warmth of her response.

Her breasts met the muscled planes of his chest and she felt his hand circle her waist as though wishing he could bind her even closer to him. She knew she had to make a decision. On one hand was a professional lifetime of building her career. On the other was the emptiness she felt, the regret for not saying yes once before.

She cleared the cobwebs of indecision from her voice, but the words still sounded husky. "You got a good sense of direction, Gerrard?"

His eyes narrowed and she watched his nostrils flare, the beat of his pulse at his throat accelerate. Slowly he nodded.

"Then I imagine you can find my bedroom."

He swept her up into his arms before the words scarcely left her mouth. The gesture made her feel light, wickedly free and wildly feminine.

Lacing her hands together behind his neck, she reveled in his easy strength as he carried her confidently into the bedroom, not wavering or searching, but plotting a direct path.

Moonlight spilled in the huge floor-to-ceiling windows. The drapes hadn't been pulled for the evening yet and the gauzy sheers lent a mysterious air to her normally staid room.

"Just as I expected," he whispered against her neck. "So like you."

"What if I'm not what you expect?" she whispered back. What if he found her plain and unexciting once the mystery of discovery faded?

"But I've always known what to expect," he said against her lips.

Always? The thought floated, niggled, then disappeared as Kenneth made slow, devastating love to her lips.

The pressure of his mouth was firm, unyielding, taking them down another path. One she'd been moving toward since they met.

Now they were racing toward that place, even though Kenneth was letting her savor each moment. The rustle of their clothing, the gentle whoosh of the air-conditioning as it drifted through the vents and the sound of their ragged breathing took the place of conversation.

For all her confidence in the courtroom, she didn't feel nearly so sure on this turf. Not that she hadn't dated since Billy, but she'd never given her heart.

It struck her then. That was what she was doing. Giving her heart...along with her trust.

She reached out to join him on the journey, to exchange touch for touch, heartbeat for heartbeat.

Her hands strayed over the bunched muscles of his shoulders, the definition of his biceps, then grazed the planes of his chest, centering on the brown nubby nipples. They quivered under her attention.

Emboldened, she traced her fingers up the hard, flat line of his stomach. She felt him shudder. Then he reached out to trace the same lines on her body.

Her eyelids fluttered shut at the pleasure he created, feeling the heat that raced through her blood, melting the bones in its path. She wondered if her trembling legs would continue to support her.

He reached out just then, pulling her to him, then taking them both to the soft pillow of her bed.

His kisses were hot and dark, his touch electric. He paused only to dispatch the remainder of their clothing. Having yearned for that completeness, she reveled in the feel of unadorned flesh touching, uniting.

Kenneth placed a kiss beneath her knee, then followed the path he blazed, making the tender flesh of her inner thigh tremble with anticipation. His lips drifted over the tumble of curls at that juncture, then moved up the curve of her abdomen, tracing the line of her rib cage, then reaching the soft fullness of her breasts.

Barbara felt her nipples harden in anticipation as his mouth closed over one breast. Unable to contain the moan that erupted, she arched toward him, gratified when he deepened his touch.

Running her hands down his back, she wanted to give, as well. When he pulled her over so that she lay on top of him, she began the same fiery trail of kisses. Rewarded with shudders that spoke silently, yet eloquently of his pleasure, she continued. She nibbled, then mouthed an array of kisses that trailed down his torso, finally reaching his leg, inching slowly down that tall column, then back upward again. Her lips tantalized the flesh near his groin and he groaned in response.

In less than a second, he'd reversed positions. Lying beneath him, her breasts flattened against his chest, her legs tangled in his, she felt their hearts beating the same rapid tattoo. Whispered words that she couldn't quite make out pressed against her neck, tumbled against her lips.

She wanted the words, but she wanted him, as well. All of him.

Again his mind was in sync with hers.

He covered her mouth with his as he plunged inside. Moistly, eagerly, she accepted his fullness. There was no surrender; rather, a strengthening as they came together, a needy passion. Both were greedy. But for each other's pleasure, rather than their own.

His movements were a deliciously slow torment, making her feel worshiped...adored. Her first climax rippled around them both. Then his strokes took them over the edge. And Barbara fell willingly, eagerly. And took her heart along for the ride.

Chapter Nine

Kenneth watched the flush of her skin, the curve of her cheek and felt the fragile walls surrounding his heart tumble.

Again.

Her eyes, sated and undeniably happy, watched him, and he wondered how transparent his thoughts were.

To distract her, he skimmed the length of her body from breast to hip in one long stroke, enjoying the shiver he created, the expression on her face that said she welcomed more.

Hers was a face that had always commanded attention. From her delicately molded nose to the cheekbones that seemed sculpted for an artist's pleasure. Huge, deeply fringed eyes of deepest midnight that invited…promised…incited. Her lips were a sensual curve, which he knew from experience had been created to drive a man mad.

And now that face smiled only for him.

A silver bath of moonlight flooded over her, highlighting the ivory cream of her skin, the curves and valleys of her body that had responded so eagerly to him.

Her incredible capacity to give was something he'd forgotten. With maturity, she might have become more reluctant to become involved, but once committed she held nothing back.

Her scent wound around his senses, as sensual and complicated as she was. She'd never been a simple woman. Once, far more open, but never someone to underestimate. The layers of her soul had acquired a wisdom beyond her years even then, and now those edges overlapped his own soul with new power.

Reaching out, he fisted a handful of her hair. It drifted over his fingers like satin and silk. Running the back of his hand over the slope of her shoulder, he recognized its velvety texture. Every memory they'd shared, sharp and sweet, swamped him.

True, they'd been younger then. But it was the mature Barbara that entranced him. She had grown into the promise she'd shown at eighteen, then surpassed it in a way even he couldn't have foreseen.

Her lips nestled on the hollow of his throat, before she drew back again. "You were right, Gerrard. No surprises."

His heart stilled for a moment. Had she guessed? "I'm not an original?"

Her fingertips traced a line down his chest, eliciting a quiver. She was the only woman who'd ever made him shudder from desire alone. That hadn't changed, but had only intensified along with her hold over him.

"I didn't say that." Her voice grew softer. "But I expected to feel wonderful, and now I'm somewhere in the vicinity of magnificent."

He remembered to breathe again. "You aren't alone, Counselor."

Her leg nudged his before she draped her torso over his. "I'm aware of that. In fact, I'm known for never overlooking the obvious."

His foot trapped hers. "Keeps you on your toes."

She laughed softly. "Not from where I'm lying." Tenderness grew in her eyes and he saw the seriousness that lurked in their dark recesses.

He wondered suddenly how he could play with her emotions this way.

And knew he couldn't.

He had to tell her. He couldn't let her go on believing a lie.

She picked up his hand, running her fingers over his. "I probably shouldn't tell you this, but I made a wish the other night." She laughed gently. "It's this silly thing I do…. But I wished I could relive a certain part of my life. When I was eighteen, actually." She met his eyes. "But now I know this is better. I wouldn't want to change my past. That was then, this is now."

"What if—"

She placed her fingers against his lips. "I think I've had enough 'what ifs.' It's time I looked to the future instead of the past."

His heart struggled with his conscience.

"And I'd like to think that future includes you," she whispered, her heart in her eyes.

And his conscience lost miserably.

"You're a tough examiner, Counselor." He couldn't repress the huskiness in his voice even though he tucked his pain deep inside. Theirs were moments etched in time…engraved in his heart. Even if they were standing on the edge of goodbye.

"I learn from the best," she replied.

"You are the best." Deciding to forget the pain and the past, at least for now, he turned her on her back, trapping her against the mattress.

He kissed the underside of her chin, the delicate hollows of her throat, then elicited a giggle when he nipped her earlobe. Laughter was returning more easily to her now. Along with a sultry sensuality that was unaffected, completely natural, and therefore devastating.

He concentrated on making those giggles turn to moans as the moonlight whispered around them…and the past shouted to be heard.

THE GENTLE SPLASH of water tumbled around them, scented with Barbara's magnolia bath salts. The oversize Jacuzzi tub was perfect for two, and Kenneth was glad she'd indulged in the luxury. Especially as he watched her dip her head forward, then back, allowing a flicker of candlelight to play over her face. The motion created shadow, then light. It was erotic. Hypnotic. And sensuous beyond his dreams.

She reached toward one candle in wonder, her face still flushed with arousal. "I can't believe you did all this. Warm, scented water. Candles. Are you sure you're for real?"

His body sidled toward hers, proving just how real. He was rewarded with a small gasp of pleasure.

"Oh, yes, Gerrard. Very, very real."

Rather than pulling her from the tub and disregarding the bed for the inviting rug that lay close by,

Kenneth picked up a soft washcloth. Her eyes shimmered and her mouth curved into an O as though of its own accord when he leisurely soaped her shoulders, then teased the length of skin on her rib cage.

However, her telling flush returned as he carefully soaped each breast, making the nipples pout for equal attention. But it was the telltale pulse at her throat that did him in. Especially when she reached out her hands, delicately searching. Gratefully finding.

It was all he could do not to take her then. Instead, he turned her around, seeing the surprise on her face as he did so. Then he cradled her between his legs, his chest to her back, his hands traveling over the curve of her hips.

"You have nice ideas, Gerrard," she murmured, leaning down to kiss the back of his hand.

It was a sweet, touching gesture and he felt the lump in his throat grow suddenly.

"You're always saying I don't know you that well, Counselor. But the truth is you really don't know me."

Her laugh was gentle as she dipped her fingers into the water and watched it splay onto his forearm. "I know all I need to." Her hands stilled for a moment. "I also know I've trespassed every professional boundary I've ever set for myself." She twisted around, placing her fingers over his lips, her eyes pleading with him to agree. "But I don't want to talk about that now."

He clenched his jaw, knowing how great his own need to talk was, but her expression told him it would be lunacy to do so now. Instead, he reached up to twirl his finger in the curl that draped beguilingly over her forehead. The rest of her hair was piled high on her head, precariously held in place by a single barrette, except for a few tendrils that curled softly near her temples.

Why couldn't she have been ugly, with a houseful of bratty kids and an obnoxious husband? Why did she have to be so damn beautiful?

She swept her thick lashes downward and he remembered that tiny touch of shyness she'd once possessed. Now it was caught up in charm and intelligence, hidden in the wealth of confidence she had acquired. Then she'd been a girl. Now she was a woman.

A complicated woman.

Her fingers were trailing over his thighs, lingering behind his knees, then traveling down his calves. The movement jangled his thoughts. His nerves. His sanity.

When she began the journey again, he stood up, pulling her along with him.

Stepping out of the tub, he reached for her and carried her into the bedroom, ignoring the puddle of water they splashed onto the floor. Wet footprints trailed behind them in the lush pile carpeting. He considered grabbing a towel, then decided against it.

Despite the cool air that greeted them, the lure of water-slickened bodies was too great. The need to unite wet, naked flesh sent them tumbling onto the bed, the polished cotton of the sheets abrading already-sensitized skin.

They came together quickly this time, disregarding tenderness. Greed outweighed gentleness. Passion overruled sensibility.

Moving together as though in practiced ease, Kenneth reached beneath her, lifting her buttocks in his hands to bring her closer. She arched toward him greedily, her long legs muscled and strong as they wrapped around him.

The sheen of moisture made her breasts slide against his chest in a sinuous dance. Catching his breath, he wondered if there had ever been another woman like her.

And knew there hadn't been.

She was the true original. He'd simply mastered his duplicity. She reached for him and he relinquished the thought, knowing only that they had now. Perhaps no more.

But there was now.

BARBARA SAT PRIMLY in her chair at the plaintiff's table. She felt Kenneth's approach and smelled the distinctive tang of his cologne before she heard him. Grateful that her client hadn't arrived yet, she slanted a smile toward Kenneth.

"You're looking mighty pleased with yourself this morning, Counselor."

"I took some good advice, Gerrard."

A corner of his mouth lifted in a grin. "What was that?"

"That I loosen up and drop my briefs."

His grin broadened. "Then I'll have to concentrate on more advice."

She gave in to the urge to flirt shamelessly. "Why? Weren't you satisfied with your first advice?"

Watching his breathing deepen, the tick in his jaw flare to life, she smiled.

"I don't know. Perhaps we should repeat the first round so I can make a better determination."

She felt some of his heat reach her. The linen of her tailored suit suddenly seemed stifling. At this rate, it was going to be a long day in court. Glancing around to make certain they were alone, she lowered her voice. "I found Hershey's Kisses instead of cereal in my Cheerios box this morning."

"Must be a new marketing strategy," he replied easily.

She met his eyes, making her own sultry. "Works for me."

He glanced pointedly at their surroundings. "You trying to torture me, Counselor?"

"Could be, Gerrard."

"Today will take forever, you know."

She shrugged, trying to appear nonchalant although silently agreeing with him. "Maybe we can manage a few minutes alone."

"What do you suggest? That we go to the storage room and take inventory of each other?"

She felt the heat of a flush building in her cheeks. It was ridiculous at her age to be embarrassed, but the truth was she'd like nothing better than to escape with him.

"Actually, I was thinking about lunch," she replied, twirling a pen between her fingers.

But he was shaking his head regretfully. "Can't. I have to meet with the board at Bakewell."

Her eyebrows lifted.

"Don't go all paranoid." He leaned forward, lowering his voice to a confidential whisper. "I'm not going there to reveal all your secrets—like the fact that you're ticklish behind one knee and not the other." He trailed his fingers over her wrist. "It's just a progress report. But tonight—"

"I have a cooking class," she interrupted, just remembering at that moment, thinking at the same time she could cancel the class. Swallowing, she regretfully moved her wrist away, knowing she had to stop his assault on her senses. It wouldn't do to forget they were in the courtroom.

"I can think of something to cook up," he replied, his expression conveying the temperature of his thoughts.

"You could go with me," she improvised, remembering she'd promised to attend and share a special recipe with one of her classmates. "And then we'd have the rest of the evening together."

"Bribery?"

"If it works, Gerrard."

"Something I'd better not let my client know," he replied dryly.

Glancing up, Barbara saw her own client headed their way. And from the expression on his face, it was clear Mr. Delight was wondering why she was having such a cozy chat with opposing counsel.

Quickly she gathered a stack of papers together, schooling her expression and making her voice brisk. "Perhaps we should take this up later."

"But—"

"Later," she whispered anxiously.

Kenneth glanced up and saw Pete Delight closing in on them. Nodding, he moved to his own chair.

Mr. Delight frowned as he sat down heavily. "I didn't know we were negotiating for a settlement."

Barbara felt a clench of apprehension, especially since she hadn't given the case a moment's thought in the past twelve hours. "We're still in place for the trial, Mr. Delight."

"I'd hoped so, with the splash in today's papers, but just now you and Mr. Gerrard didn't look to be on opposite sides."

"It's only on television that the lawyers are slicing and dicing each other every moment. It's smarter to do business when you can be civil with the other side."

He slanted a glance at her. "Is that advice for my benefit, little lady? After my brawl with Matthews?" Mr. Delight gingerly patted his side. "I can still feel your last subtle hint."

She kept her tone purposely even, free of expression. "Be assured that your legal representation is as sharp as ever."

"Better be, little lady. If my case is compromised, you will be, too."

Compromised. The word rang in her conscience.

Although used to threats, idle or otherwise, from self-important clients, Barbara wasn't accustomed to feeling the spurt of guilt that said she'd blurred the lines between professional and personal. Even though she'd questioned herself, demanded strict guidelines, she hadn't expected to be reprimanded by her client.

Certain after last night that she could control both aspects, now she wondered. Warmed until a moment ago by the memory of the previous evening, now Mr. Delight's words chilled her.

Glancing over at Kenneth, she doubted she could relinquish her relationship with him. At the same time, she wondered if she could sacrifice a career-making case.

Should she resign from the case? And who would benefit? She would be costing both the client and her firm. No other attorneys in her firm were prepared to step in and take over for her. It had taken months of preparation to acquaint herself with the issues, to know them as well as she knew... Her thoughts scattered suddenly. As well as she was *beginning* to know Kenneth.

You said "no" once before, an inner voice warned. What did that get you?

Regret.

Cold and lonely, regret spun insidiously, endlessly. It was part of why she'd turned to Kenneth. Why she considered giving up everything else that was important to her.

The clerk called for the court to rise as the judge entered, his robes billowing as he strode to the bench. Carefully Barbara filed her thoughts away. Mentally compartmentalizing them—one of her greatest strengths as an attorney. Realizing as she did that it was no longer an easy task.

BARBARA WAS STILL QUIET as they entered the cooking school. She'd noticed Kenneth's concerned glances, but she hadn't revealed the thoughts that had plagued her all day. Even confiding them to him would be compromising her client. It was an untenable position, she realized. One she still wasn't sure how to resolve.

To his credit, Kenneth hadn't plagued her with questions, seeming to tune in to her reflective mood.

Chatter, along with the sound of spoons hitting bowls and knives being sharpened, traveled down the corridor. The pungent aroma of chopped onion and garlic competed with fresh basil and rosemary. The sizzle of pure butter and rich olive oil greeted them, as well.

"Are we late, Counselor?"

"No, some people come early to try out their new recipes before class. The teacher doesn't mind—it's a great way to get the onions chopped ahead of time." She smiled, thinking that this class had once been the highlight of her week. Now it seemed like a distraction, despite the burdens weighing heavily on her mind.

He tweaked her nose, then slid an arm around her waist. "Good to see you smiling. Looked like you were carrying around a Tonka truck full of cement."

She did smile then, not a full smile, but she couldn't shed her worries that easily. "Only a Tonka toy truck?"

"I'd hate to see you buried under half a ton of cement. Might mess up that razor-sharp lady lawyer look."

Frowning, she glanced down at her suit. "I can't always ditch my occupation when it's convenient."

Kenneth whistled. "Whoa. Hit a nerve, I see."

"Barbara! You've got to taste this! It's my best effort yet!" An elf of a man, all white hair and whiskers, stood expectantly just inside the door, beaming with anticipation and pride. He held out a tasting spoon.

"Tony!" Barbara turned distracted eyes from Kenneth to her classmate—one of her favorites, the one she'd promised the recipe to. "Great to see you. Let me introduce Kenneth Gerrard."

The two men shook hands around the spoon.

Barbara shared her smile with both men. "Kenneth would love to taste your newest creation, wouldn't you, Kenneth?"

She had the distinct impression that he was gritting his teeth, but his mouth eased into a smile. "I'd be privileged, Tony."

Kenneth took the spoon. Barbara watched and waited.

Kenneth tasted, swallowed, then blanched. His face twisted before he managed to look duly appreciative. She suspected it took quite an effort for him not to shudder. While Tony was an enthusiastic cook, his imaginative combination of spices and foods such as garlic- and basil-seasoned Apple Bake could be pure torture. Thinking about the last time she'd been his guinea pig made her wince for Kenneth.

"Thanks, Tony." Kenneth slanted her a telling glance. "And you, too, Barbara."

She suspected he intended to return the favor, but then they were swept into the class. The instructor asked the students to take their places. A general buzz ensued as greetings were exchanged, aprons donned and stations readied.

Confident and remarkably at ease, Kenneth took his place next to Barbara, offering the teacher a smile that had her obviously melting.

Suzanne Sims, the instructor, was an attractive woman in her early fifties who tried valiantly to look forty. Her blond hair was a touch too platinum to be real. But she exercised regularly, keeping her voluptuous figure in shape, despite the delicacies she sampled in her cooking classes. And it was clear she fancied the new addition to the class.

"Barbara, would you like to introduce your *friend?*" Suzanne purred, never taking her gaze from Kenneth.

Making the perfunctory introductions, Barbara suddenly saw Kenneth through the teacher's eyes. Glancing around, she noticed a healthy amount of interest on the part of most of the female students, as well. Slanting a glance at Kenneth, she realized that he recognized the attention. And he was enjoying it.

In fact, he winked at Suzanne as he smiled broadly.

Barbara felt a slow burn building and recognized the emotion with surprise. She was jealous because other women were showing interest in Kenneth!

He tipped his head just then, granting her a private smile that said his only interest was in her. And the swoosh of relief that hit her stomach made it clear that her feelings for him were growing, leaping and spinning out-of-bounds.

Suzanne clapped her hands together. "Let's get started." She ticked off items on her fingers. "Bowls, knives..." Her voice trailed off momentarily. "Mr. Gerrard, you can take the station next to mine. Otherwise you won't be able to participate. And I'm sure that Barbara wants you to enjoy your evening with us."

Shrugging, Kenneth disguised his smile as he moved toward the front of the room. Barbara fumed silently, but dutifully pulled out a mixing bowl from beneath her station. Tony passed her a plate of chopped onions, garlic, leeks and celery.

''Thanks,'' she managed to mutter.

The older man rewarded her with a thumbs-up sign, and she smiled, distracted for a moment.

As Suzanne settled into her teacher's role, she discussed the dishes they would be cooking that night. One was a chopped veal concoction that sounded suspiciously like meat loaf. As Suzanne outlined the recipes, Kenneth obligingly held up each ingredient, looking like an oversize, burly magician's assistant.

But the class appreciated his humor, laughing as he came up with more and more inventive ways to showcase each item. Rolling her eyes, Barbara fell in with the humor, as well. Admiring his complete lack of self-consciousness, she giggled as he brandished a zucchini as though he fenced with an invisible opponent. It was hard to believe that this was the same high-powered attorney who made his colleagues shake with fear at the thought of facing him in court. Apparently cooking school was a less formidable battleground.

That or the bedroom.

The thought popped into her head, warmed her down to her toes and then lingered to send a mellow feeling of content through her.

Just then Kenneth juggled two cantaloupes, making it appear that he held a dozen rather than the easily managed duo. Then he pretended to drop one, rescuing it at the last moment. Instead of admonishing him, Suzanne joined in with the laughter of the other students.

Barbara's own lips curved into a smile despite the riot of emotions he caused. She'd always had a weakness for the class clown. Starting with Billy. Now...

Her eyes widened. In some ways, it was as though she'd recaptured Billy. Kenneth was as much of a class clown as Billy had been. Then she shook away the thought. It wasn't fair to Kenneth to continue comparing them. Especially since he was no substitute.

He grinned at her and waved.

No, Kenneth didn't need to stand-in for anyone else. She loved him for himself.

And she did.

Hopelessly, irretrievably.

When had the game turned into something deeper, richer?

Feeling her heart clutch, then open to chasmlike proportions, Barbara watched Kenneth as he continued entertaining the class. As she watched, he would turn suddenly, sending her that special, intimate smile that said his thoughts centered around her.

Suzanne simpered, the class giggled and Barbara kept falling in love. Maybe Dani had been right. Fate, destiny, whatever you wanted to call it, had handed her another chance. One she didn't have to turn down.

One she didn't want to turn down.

Chapter Ten

Kenneth reached his hotel room when a familiar, fine-tuned sixth sense kicked in. The prickle of hair on the back of his neck made him pause and stare at the closed door. It had been years. Still…

The door swung open suddenly and Kenneth silently cursed as his adrenaline kicked in. His hands balled into fists as he assumed an offensive stance.

"Hold on! It's just me."

Kenneth released a pent-up breath along with a healthy curse as he stared at his brother. "Eric! What the hell are you doing here?"

"Nice to see you, too," Eric replied mildly.

Kenneth plowed a hand through his styled hair, ruining the carefully cultivated look. "You know better than to surprise me, Brother."

Eric stepped back, allowing Kenneth into the room. "If you'd return your messages, I wouldn't be here."

Kenneth avoided his brother's scrutiny. "I got sidetracked."

"That's apparent. But you know the rules." Eric's eyes were steady, unrelenting. The eyes of the oldest brother. And despite adulthood, the same concern still lurked there. "Those rules haven't changed."

Kenneth moved restlessly toward the window. "As you can see, I'm fine. A little confused maybe, but that's all."

"Spill it."

Kenneth laughed humorlessly. "Refreshing to see you're still as blunt as ever."

Eric focused midnight dark eyes on his brother. "I didn't fly across the country to exchange pleasantries. Is there a problem? One we should all know about?"

Kenneth sighed, knowing he had broken rules he'd lived by for more than a decade. And meeting his brother's unblinking stare, he also knew it would be good to have someone to confide in. That in itself was a rarity.

"Barbara Callister is here."

Eric's brows shot up as he narrowed his gaze. "You contacted her?"

"She's opposing counsel on the case I'm handling." Briefly Kenneth outlined how he'd seen Barbara's name on the documents, then garnered the case for his own, and told Eric about the subsequent events since they'd met. "And now I'm in deep...too deep."

"How did she react to seeing you again?"

Kenneth turned his head, staring out the window, barely seeing the magnificent display. "She didn't recognize me."

"But you just said—"

Kenneth couldn't keep the bitterness from his voice. "Despite that, she doesn't know who I really am."

"Why haven't you told her?"

Good question. One he'd asked himself a thousand times already. "I intended to. Then I deliberately waited, hoping she'd know who I was...believing she had to somehow know." Kenneth unclenched his hands. "Now it's too late."

"It's never too late to set things right."

Kenneth stared at his brother in disbelief. "What do I say? Hey, now that I've duped you and seduced you, guess what? I'm Billy Duncan. Want to go back in the past with me? Forget what a jerk I've been lately? Forget that I took your trust and stomped it to pieces?"

"Smooth talker," Eric replied dryly. "Why not tell her what happened? That you didn't have any choice in the past? That you don't have much more of a choice now?"

Kenneth rubbed his jaw, then let his hand drop to his side. "Even this meeting is a risk. How can I compromise our entire family?"

Eric weighed his answer heavily. "Can you trust her?"

"I think so...." *But enough to risk his entire family's safety?*

"She's a responsible attorney. Surely she understands how the Witness Protection Program works."

"Logically, no problem. But convincing her that I couldn't contact her for fifteen years might be different. Then she won't be dealing with an intellectual issue, but an emotional one."

"And it's not an emotional issue for the rest of us? Hiding, changing our identities? Being afraid to fall in love and have a family because we draw someone else into the danger? Having to split the family unit and spread ourselves around the country so we no longer resembled the Duncan family? And still having to live as though *we* belonged to the Mafia, instead of being openly proud that our father had the guts to bring down a mobster?'' Eric caught Kenneth's gaze and held it. ''Bottom line, if you love her, you have to tell her the truth.''

''I never stopped loving her,'' Kenneth admitted. ''I shoved her memory to the background, but seeing her again...knowing her now...''

''Then you have to be the one to decide. If you're wrong, you jeopardize all of us. If you're right, it could be your best shot at happiness.''

''And if she can't accept that I haven't told her so far?''

''From what I remember of Barbara, she might be angry with you, but I don't think she'd blow the cover on the rest of us. But it's your call, Brother.''

As he well knew. ''I threw out an ultimatum that night. I told her if she wouldn't elope, that we were through. I thought I could force her to say yes. I never dreamed it would be the last thing I'd say to her. Then I disappeared for fifteen years without a word. How can she accept any explanation this late in coming?''

''If she loves you, she might be glad to know that silence saved your life.''

Kenneth gazed at his brother, knowing the woman Eric loved at the time had chosen not to live a life filled with risk. And Eric had been the one to relocate on the East Coast, far from the rest of the family, in a move designed to totally disguise the former Duncan family unit. Luckily Kenneth had gone to school at Harvard, and they'd had some contact.

But it was a lonely existence. Friends couldn't be brought into the confidence. It was a danger for them as well as the Duncans. Which is what Billy had been cautioned when they were swept into the program fifteen years ago. Raging, he'd insisted on telling Barbara and had been told the knowledge would endanger her as well as the rest of the family. It was too raw, too fresh. They would be lucky to escape the long arm of the mob, but no one else could know.

And if Barbara was involved, she could be equally at risk. Angered, then anguished, he'd had to make a decision that would affect the rest of his life. And he'd had to believe that it was the right decision.

But now there was Barbara again.

And he loved her. More than he worried about any risk for himself. He met Eric's unblinking gaze. But he had the rest of his family to worry about still.

Eric laid a heavy, but comforting hand on his shoulder. "Still your call."

Kenneth's voice was somber. "And I'm no closer to knowing what to do."

Eric quirked an unexpected smile. "Try humor. That's always worked for you."

Kenneth affectionately slugged his brother. "I'll remind you about that the next time you complain about my best practical joke so far."

Eric groaned. "I have a feeling the next one will be coming soon."

Kenneth laughed, then gripped his brother's hand in a firm shake. "Thanks for the advice. I don't see you often enough, you know."

"Pull another disappearing act, kid, and you'll remember *I'm* the big brother."

Kenneth wished for the millionth time that things could have been different, that their family hadn't been ripped apart. And then he wished, too, for wisdom. Because he had to decide whether to tell Barbara the truth.

BARBARA CHECKED her appearance in the full-length mirror inside her bedroom door, adjusted the tailored red silk blouse and then, satisfied, took one last sip of coffee before grabbing her briefcase from the hall. She had just enough time to go over this morning's exhibits before court time.

Slinging her purse over her shoulder, she reached for the doorknob and twisted it.

The door remained steadfastly closed.

Frowning, she twisted the knob again. Nothing happened.

Not sure what to think, she yanked on the knob.

It didn't move.

Pitching her briefcase and purse on the floor, she used both hands to attack the knob. The door didn't budge.

She grabbed a nearby chair, disregarding the fact that it was a valued antique, and stood on it, peering out of the half circle of glass at the top of the door. It took her a moment, then she realized that the door had been taped shut.

What in the world?

Better question, who in the world? But then, that was a question that didn't need answering.

She was going to kill him.

Looking around for another escape route, she realized there wasn't one. Her apartment was on the tenth floor and, while French doors opened on to the balcony, there was no exit other than the front door.

Feeling like an idiot, she realized she would have to call someone for help. The building manager? Or 911? Oh, this was going to be hugely embarrassing.

A knock thundered on the door.

"Fire department! You call for help, lady?"

Barbara put her eye to the peephole. Kenneth stood outside, dressed in an Armani suit, a fireman's hat on his head, waving an ax. She searched for justified anger as a wave of giggles erupted.

"Don't worry, ma'am. We'll have you out in no time. Obviously the work of terrorists."

The sound of tape being unpeeled reached through the door.

"That or a sick mind, ma'am. Never know who we're dealing with these days."

Barbara reached again for anger. At the same moment, Kenneth swung open the door. "Women and children first. Got any babies I can rescue?" He flashed her a wide grin. "That'd look great on my résumé."

Giggles won over anger. "You are the most hopeless, idiotic..."

"Someone once told me that humor was a great icebreaker."

"Did that same person also tell you that I have to be in court early today?"

Kenneth scratched his chin. "Those fonts of wisdom can run dry every once in a while."

"Consider it arid, Gerrard." But a soft smile curved her lips. "Nice to see you first thing in the morning."

"And the last thing at night," he murmured, reaching out to kiss her. The fireman's helmet clanked between them.

Barbara rubbed her forehead. "Careful, Captain Courageous, that thing's dangerous."

He winked lasciviously. "Glad you noticed, ma'am."

"You *are* hopeless." Flushing with a renewed heat, she straightened her already-immaculate suit and fussed with her purse as she bent to retrieve it.

"Is that any kind of gratitude?" he asked with a wounded expression, the light in his eyes giving him away. "After that stellar rescue?"

She wished they didn't have to be in court. She pictured the sweet-smelling sheets she'd just put on the bed, and imagined rumpling those fresh linens.

A sigh escaped as she leaned against him. "You're a bad influence, Gerrard."

Pulling off the helmet and dropping it with a gentle thud on the carpeted floor, he reached out to twirl the hair that she'd left loose and free. "I hope so, Counselor."

"Not denying it?"

He hooked his thumbs behind her neck, massaging the sensitive spots there. "No point, when you've got me dead to rights."

Her breath grew thready. "Case closed, Gerrard?"

He moved his hands down her back and over her hips. "Not completely, I hope."

Her lips opened to accept his kiss, tasting an unexpected desperation. At odds with his humor, that darker emotion flavored his kiss, drew her deeper to the crest he was riding.

A wave of memories triggered suddenly. The desperation in Billy's last kiss, those final moments. When she could draw back, Barbara stared into Kenneth's eyes, struck by the similarities between his and Billy's. But Kenneth had distinctly green eyes, while Billy's had been an unforgettable shade of blue.

Shaking her head to dislodge the confusing thoughts, she credited them to the wave of passion that swept over her while in Kenneth's arms. Since she'd only given her heart twice, she supposed it was normal to compare the experiences. Much like the sense of déjà vu that had accompanied her entire relationship with Kenneth.

He gave her one last, reluctant kiss. "If you're going to be on time, we'd better get going. While you check your lipstick, I'll go stash the ax and helmet."

Her fingers flew automatically to her lips. Just thinking about their kiss caused a warm rosy flush all over again.

Then he gathered his props, waved and disappeared. In a few short minutes, she checked and repaired her makeup and was out the door. She wished Kenneth had stuck around. They could have driven to court together.

Slipping her keys from her purse, she fingered them as she walked toward her car. Humming, she inserted her key into the door lock and found it wouldn't go all the way in. Frowning, she glanced at the key and then looked, *really* looked at her car.

The locks were taped shut.

Beneath the tape appeared to be at least a ton of confetti. Carefully applied only to the locks, the tape wouldn't hurt the car's finish, but how was she going to get her car door open? Despite the grin tugging at her lips, she knew she should be mad.

A horn tooted and she whirled around.

Kenneth grinned at her from the open space of his convertible, the top rolled back and down. "Need a ride, lady?"

Sauntering over to his car, she leveled him with a mock glare. "What I need, apparently, is a large investment in the local tape business. I could make a fortune."

"I haven't kidnapped you in a while. Thought you were due."

She glanced back at her decorated car. "You have a definite way of making a statement, Gerrard."

His eyes met and locked on hers. "I'm just beginning to talk, Counselor."

Warmth curled, then raced through her bloodstream.

He reached over and opened the door. Feigning reluctance, she slid in beside him. "Going my way, Gerrard?"

Cupping her chin, he studied her lips. "Always."

Instead of a quick, cocky gesture, he placed a gentle, searching kiss on her lips.

Once again at odds with the whimsical morning he'd provided, she wondered. But he was easing back, then shifting the car into forward, letting the sleek vehicle eat up the miles of concrete.

The sky was an incomparable field of unending blue, interrupted occasionally by a burst of nonthreatening clouds of purest white. Sunshine poured over the mountains, drenching the city. Glancing over at

Kenneth, Barbara knew she'd like nothing better than to ditch the trial proceedings and play hooky.

Studying his face, she was surprised by the serious set to his jaw. She couldn't see his eyes because they were shaded by designer sunglasses, but she suspected the expression there was serious, as well. Once again she wondered why.

She enjoyed the ride, the luxury of having someone else battle the traffic. While the congestion wasn't on the level of L.A.'s or Houston's, there was an annoying surplus of cars on the freeway. She'd always enjoyed the independence of driving her own car, the freedom to come and go as she pleased. But there was something infinitely more pleasurable about sharing that ride with Kenneth.

Settling back, she listened to the comfortable oldies station Kenneth had tuned in. A song by the Beach Boys ended and the disc jockey began talking, segueing into the next commercial.

She started to automatically tune out the advertisement when the disc jockey's words in the commercial began to penetrate as the obviously amateur commercial began. *"Every Ken needs his Barbie. Won't you be my doll?"*

Then the disc jockey jokingly commented, "Those were the words of one of our city's lovesick in a special plea to his ladylove."

Barbara swiveled her head to stare at Kenneth as the commercial continued, a blatant ad that spelled out Ken's desire for Barbie.

Clearing her throat, she angled her head toward him. "Tell me you didn't do that."

"What?"

"Don't play innocent, Gerrard. That commercial just now." It hit her suddenly, his perfect timing. Taping her in the apartment, then her car. It had ensured that she would be sitting beside him when the advertisement aired.

"Like it?" he asked, completely unabashed.

"I...I..." She didn't know. It was so unexpected, so out of character for her carefully cultivated image. But then, no one she knew would identify her as the Barbie Ken must have.

"Don't sweat it, Counselor. It'll be our little secret."

Barbara couldn't resist glancing at the cars surrounding them, wondering how many of the occupants were smirking and laughing over the commercial.

"You really think your fellow commuters have time to worry about one little commercial?" he asked, navigating into the outside lane. "Or to speculate whether the people are real?"

"They are real, though, aren't they?" she asked in a quiet voice.

Kenneth crossed lanes, smoothly exiting into downtown Salt Lake. He took his eyes from the traffic. "Very real."

A semitruck honked and Kenneth returned his attention to the road. As they neared the streets leading to the courthouse, the traffic increased considerably.

"I wonder if something's going on," Barbara commented as they got closer to the courthouse. "It's usually not this crowded."

"Any big murder cases in town?" Kenneth asked, turning down a side street.

"No. Must be something else."

After parking, they walked toward the huge stone building. Barbara resisted the urge to lean closer to Kenneth, to pretend they were strolling toward a date rather than a day in court. But her client could be nearby, and she didn't need another confrontation with him.

They rounded the corner, nearing the steps leading to the courthouse. Suddenly a pack of reporters rushed up to them, shouting, waving microphones and positioning video cameras.

"Miss Callister, can you tell us more about Cookiegate?"

"When do we hear your version, Mr. Gerrard?"

"Is there more to this case than cookies?"

"Mr. Gerrard, any truth to Mr. Delight's allegations?"

An array of similar requests burst from the eager group of reporters as they pushed closer, surrounding them.

"This will be played out in court, not the news media," Kenneth responded curtly.

Taking Barbara's arm, he carved a path for them to the door.

One reporter took a last, parting shot. "You two really on opposite sides?"

The tic in Kenneth's jaw increased, but other than that he remained expressionless. They pushed inside, followed by the pack of hungry reporters. Kenneth shouldered his way into a room reserved for attorneys.

As the door closed behind them, Kenneth jerked a thumb outward toward the reporters still roaming the hall. "I want you to know I didn't have any idea they'd be here."

She glanced at him in surprise. "I know that. I hardly think you'd orchestrate a special morning like today's only to have it end like this. You really think I trust you so little?"

A pained expression crossed his face. "Look, Barbara, I need to—"

The door shoved open and a disheveled Dani tumbled through the opening. "Jeez, what gives? They run out of real news?"

Barbara laughed, a strained, unnatural sound. "Looks like my plan backfired," she explained, thinking of her news release to the reporter.

Kenneth's head shot up sharply.

Thinking to intercept his reaction, Barbara held up one hand. "Nothing more than we talked about."

Dani's eyes widened as she looked between them. Then her gaze narrowed on Barbara in a distinct questioning look.

Barbara sighed inwardly. This was truly becoming a no-win situation.

Chapter Eleven

The shimmering water of Willard Bay was still, with no Jet Skis or powerboats roaring by. It wasn't quite the season yet. But that didn't seem to matter to Kenneth. Barbara suspected he would tackle most anything. Nothing seemed to intimidate him. But actually the fact that it was early in the season gave them unexpected privacy. The canoe Kenneth had rented was as still and quiet as the water it sat upon.

To Barbara, this was an unexpected treasure. Silence, beauty and Kenneth. All three filled her soul. He had been unusually quiet, even though the canoe trip had been his idea. She wondered about his reflective mood. He had been that way for days.

But she wondered even more about herself.

Unlike a few months ago, even a few weeks ago, now she welcomed the intrusion on her work schedule. She hadn't even hesitated when he'd suggested this outing. Just like the previous evening, when first they'd giggled through the romantic but silly movie she had reluctantly chosen and then danced the night away. And it would have been the perfect weekend to pore over statutes and case files—to grasp at the discipline and structure that had been her life. Instead, it had been easy to let the opportunity slide away.

Too easy.

Glancing at the perfectly sculpted planes of his face, she didn't regret her decision, despite the divided loyalties that tore at her. Instead, she dipped her hands into the water, letting her fingers trail over the surface.

A fish glided by, undisturbed by the human company.

"I guess they're used to people," Barbara commented, her voice as soft as their surroundings.

"That, or he thinks you're bait."

Barbara jerked her hand out of the water as Kenneth smirked, a devilish expression covering his face.

"I guess he's not exactly 'Jaws,' is he?" she remarked wryly as she relaxed again.

"No. But he can get his own lady." Kenneth held the paddle still as he leaned forward and kissed her.

When she pulled back, she looked at everything but him. She risked dipping her hands in the water again, wondering how she would resolve the dilemma he'd brought into her life.

Each time she glanced at him, the intensity in his eyes seemed to grow, deepening as though thousands of demons pursued him. It made her wonder what gnawed at him so.

Yet almost at the same time he could slip into that easy charm of his, make her forget they had tough decisions to face. But perhaps that was why he seemed uncomfortable, haunted.

Maybe he was trying to decide how to say goodbye.

The possibility stilled something deep inside.

Hugging her arms to her chest suddenly, she tried to guess what was going on inside his head, beneath his inscrutable expression.

"Cold?" he asked with concern, slowing the canoe.

She shook her head. "Just thinking."

"Should I be worried?" he asked, only partially in jest.

"Should *I?*" she countered.

The paddling came to a standstill. Only the ripples of the lake surrounding them competed with the cries of waterfowl in the silence that followed. The dent in his chin deepened as his lips thinned. "Are you trying to tell me something, Barbara?"

"I'm trying to prepare myself in case *you* are."

His brow lifted in silent query.

"In case you're trying to find a way to extricate yourself from a sticky situation."

He issued a shaky breath. "Putting words in my mouth, Counselor?"

"Then you're not trying to say goodbye?"

A multitude of emotions chased across his face as he abruptly dropped the paddle and grasped her arms. "I'm trying to do everything *except* say goodbye."

His kiss was hard, uncompromising, an unspoken stamp of possessiveness.

And Barbara let herself believe, for now, that it would be all right.

SHADOWS SIDLED against the walls, drifted over the carpet and lingered on the hollows of their hungering bodies. Ivory skin contrasted with tanned, creating sensuous foils as they reached for one another.

Kenneth closed his eyes for a moment, allowing just her scent to overwhelm his senses. The smell of late-afternoon sunshine warmed her hair, blending with the crush of wildflowers he'd tucked behind her ear. What would he do without this woman? Just as she had fifteen years ago, she'd inched under his skin, intruded on his soul.

He reached out a hand to cup her chin. Her eyes lifted to his and he saw the complete trust she'd once labored to withhold. The openness he'd worked to achieve. Now both were free, flowing. And completely undeserved. How could she trust again, once she learned of his deceit?

Still, he allowed his hands to drift over the hollows of her throat, the fragile collarbones, the vulnerable line between her breasts. She leaned toward him, escalating his desire, multiplying his guilt.

"You're bad for me, Gerrard."

The words stirred his conscience. "More than you know."

She rolled beside him, placing her hand square on his chest. "Bad enough that I've ignored my work all weekend."

"Bad enough that we can pretend for now there is no work?" He placed a hand over one breast, rubbing her nipple between his thumb and finger. Her moan answered him.

He rolled next to her, positioning her back against the mattress, trapping her legs beneath the heavy weight of his own thighs. He needed to dominate, to show her the extent of his need, his desire, his over-powering wish to possess.

The sweet smell of verbena emanated from the lux-urious sheets, mixing with the wanton smell of musky desire. All he could see, all he could feel was Barbara. The years fell away and the love grew, arrowing a path straight to his heart.

Her skin beneath his searching hands was all silk and satin.

Then silk and satin turned to fire and wonder.

Her hips were a sloping invitation, her abdomen a beguiling curve that led to the tangle of her sex. Moist and slick, she awaited him, welcomed him, consumed him. Purposely he held back, lengthening the mo-ment, cementing the memories.

He murmured her name into the sweep of her hair, caressed the silky strands. Greedily he devoured her lips, invaded the recesses of her mouth, staked a claim he knew he couldn't preserve.

Her fingers gripped his shoulders, moved restlessly over his back, then clutched his hips. Feeling her shudder, an unspeakable pleasure tore through him. She shook under his hands, the wild demand of his mouth. Despite his desperate need to conquer, he sensed her vulnerability, her quickening sense that this time was different.

So very different.

Yet she willingly tilted her head back as he skimmed the length of her throat. He was stunned by the taste of her, gorging on her essence like a starving man at his last meal.

She was, at turns, pliant, seducing, dazzling.

Despite his urgency, he forced himself to be lazily

patient as he laved his tongue over every secret recess. Each gasp, the trembling that set her afire, ignited him further.

Staggered by her answering tenderness, he was swamped with rampant emotion. His palms filled with her breasts, his mouth sought hers. Then he pulled back, capturing her eyes, staring as though to memorize each feature.

"You are mine, Barbara Callister."

She murmured half-audible sounds, whispered endearments that gripped his heart. The blood thundered in his head, echoed in his loins.

He watched as she caught her breath, saw the heavy-lidded look of completion as her body bowed, then slid limply into replete languor.

His own climax was explosive. Devastating. The power of it stunned him. As did the need. It was like a whipcord coiled inside, scarcely hesitating before striking again. In the aftermath he didn't roll away from her.

Instead, he allowed his weight to settle, making certain that he wasn't causing her discomfort. His thumb skimmed over her cheek, rested in the bow of her lips as he watched her lashes flutter before she opened her eyes to signal her satisfaction. Warm, heavy and sensual, they raked over him.

Combined with the relaxed, accepting position of her body, he could tell she welcomed the closeness. Perhaps needed it as much as he. His chest pressed against her breasts, his hipbones abraded hers and purposely he didn't withdraw, relishing this ultimate intimacy.

Her fingers sifted through his hair, then caressed

his jaw. Her breath was a mere sigh, her words a husky whisper. "I love you, Gerrard."

His heart skidded to a halt, then beat so rapidly, it threatened to cave in the walls of his chest. He couldn't pretend any longer. It was more than wrong. The deceit was savaging his soul. Regret spun over him, cobwebs of the past and present, obscuring, confusing.

Combing through the memories, he reached for one. To his relief, it clarified. With utmost care and gentleness, he reached out to touch the heart-shaped locket she wore. It was the one he'd given her the night before he'd been forced to disappear from her life.

With ease, he opened the intricate, trick fastening, exposing the two pictures inside.

Barbara's eyes opened in shock, her heart stilling. "How did you know the way it opened?" She had shared the secret of opening the locket with only one other person. And Billy had vanished, taking that knowledge with him.

His thumb eased over the two photos inside the locket. "You've kept the pictures of you...and Billy."

Stunned, Barbara reached out to touch the face that had once been so familiar. The planes and edges were harder now, more honed, and the chestnut mustache covering his full lips disguised him further.

The niggling sensation she felt when she first saw Ken dressed in a T-shirt and jeans struck her with renewed force. Even though he wasn't whipcord slim as Billy had been, it dawned on her that with maturity he could have gained the muscles and definition, even the additional height. The blond hair was now dark. She'd discounted the vague feelings of déjà vu, yet everything about him suddenly seemed familiar. But the eyes... He couldn't change the eyes.

Withdrawing, he sat up and turning aside, reached toward his face, cupping his hands near his eyes. When he turned back, she glanced in disbelief from the colored contacts in his hands to the brilliant blue of the eyes that stared at her. Filled with foreboding and a glimmer of hope, they were Billy's eyes.

And he was, indisputably Billy Duncan.

He was the young man she'd given her heart to, and the one who had broken that heart. The boy and the man blurred into one. Almost without thinking, she reached to touch his earlobe, feeling the distinctive scar where his ear had been pierced. A vision of him throwing his head back, the diamond stud in his ear glinting stunned her.

But shock was dissipating, replaced by a steadily growing sense of being tricked. Anger overrode any pleasure at discovering that Billy was alive and well.

And masquerading as Kenneth Gerrard.

She was too angry to even wonder how that had come about. She didn't need or want to know what game he played. All she knew was that she'd exposed her heart and he'd sliced it to ribbons. She rose from the tangle of sheets, overwhelmed momentarily by the pleasures they'd shared there. The love she thought she'd found.

"Barbara, please—"

"Please what?" In the act of fleeing the bed, she whirled around, the sheet pirouetting at her feet. "Am I supposed to be impressed by your Oscar caliber performance? Applaud your ingenuity?'' Her voice cracked. ''Reward you for liberating me, parading my emotions like trophies you've collected? Not once, but twice?'' Tears glimmered, gathering to tremble in the wells of her eyes. ''Sorry. But even *I* can't be had again.''

She slammed the bathroom door behind her. Inside, she staggered toward the counter, clinging to her anger, relinquishing it for the pain that struck her. White-hot shards of anguish sliced through her. Grief lodged in her throat, making it ache unbearably around the tears collecting there.

Blindly reaching toward the sink, she twisted the knob and plunged her hands into the cold water. Throwing water on her face, she disregarded her carefully applied makeup. The water seemed to sting her hot face, blending with the scalding tears that refused to stop pouring. Slowly lifting her head, she stared in the mirror.

Stark and pale, her face reflected the shock and misery she felt. Cautiously lifting one hand, she pushed back the tumble of hair that fell forward. Then she paused, staring at the reflection of her own eyes.

Betrayed.

The pain pierced her anew, and she wondered that her heart didn't lie in pieces at her feet. With trembling hands she gathered her clothing and somehow dressed. The fifty feet or so to the front door stretched out like miles of hot coals to be crossed on bare, vulnerable feet. Inhaling deeply, she reached for the doorknob and pulled the bathroom door open.

''Barbara, please. Let me explain. I know how this must look to you. I never meant to hurt you—''

"Then you've failed miserably." With great effort she repressed the hitch in her voice, the hole in her heart. Holding her dignity intact, knowing it was the only way to keep her sanity, to not shriek in pain, she refused to look at him. Striding toward the door, she didn't even pause as she gripped the doorknob.

"Barbara?" He saw the trace of tears on her face and cursed himself for her heartache, even as he knew he couldn't let her walk out of his life.

She kept her face toward the blank wood of the door. "I can't say I'll never see you again because, despite what I want, I have to face you in court. But that's all, Gerrard. Everything else is finished."

"Barbara, please. Don't go. Let me explain...."

The echo of the door quietly closing reverberated in his heart. He would have preferred the anger of her slamming the door. Instead, the quiet, finalized motion was far more damning.

Shoving both hands through his hair, he cursed vehemently as he reached for a shirt and pulled it on. Stalking onto the balcony, he searched the darkness for answers and knew there weren't any. Seeing her tears, feeling her pain, knowing it matched his own, he wondered how he could have caused it again.

IN THE DAYS that followed, Kenneth began to believe Barbara had meant what she'd said. He tried to talk to her and was met with a blank, cold wall. If what he had to say didn't involve the case, she simply wouldn't speak to him. At first he thought it would be impossible for her to completely shut him out. She couldn't spend hours every day in the same courtroom and avoid him.

Yet she did.

The isolation stripped away his pride, revealed the heartache that he couldn't hide. Still she didn't respond. Cold, polite and remote, she didn't begin to resemble the warm-blooded woman he knew her to be. She hadn't simply reverted back to how she'd been at the beginning of the trial. Instead, she was frozen—an impenetrable wall of derision.

He saw it in her eyes, along with the hurt she carefully cloaked. Beneath her thin veneer of control, he saw the questions, the confusion. Yet she blocked all his attempts to reach her. She screened her calls and never returned his messages. Her doorbell remained unanswered.

Desperate, he chased down Dani as she left the courthouse.

Hearing her name called, she turned and he saw the barriers going up as she recognized him. "Hello." She was curt, impatient.

"Are you busy, Dani?"

"Would it matter? Don't you go after whatever you want, regardless of the cost?"

Her words cut to the heart of the matter and he couldn't prevent an involuntary flinch. He decided to be equally blunt. "I can't get her to talk to me."

Dani's eyes and voice were accusing. "Do you blame her?"

"No," he replied honestly.

She shifted her briefcase and stared at the flowers neatly tended in a bed near the sidewalk. "So, what do you want now?"

"Another chance."

"Three strikes and you're out. Sounds like you've used up some mighty big ones already."

"I've used up more than I deserve. But she deserves answers, as well."

Dani stared at him directly. "I don't know exactly what happened, but you hurt her. Badly."

He felt a direct hit in his gut at the acknowledgment. He knew he'd hurt her, had anguished over his blunders. He thought about her suffering. And knew he had to offer her an explanation, a way to mend that pain. "I need one more chance. She *deserves* one more chance."

Dani weighed his words, obviously turning over the alternatives in her mind. "If you blow this one…"

"I won't," he interjected eagerly.

She watched the relief and hope flare in his expression, then sighed in acceptance. "This is your last chance, buddy. Even the Mounties won't be able to find you this time, if you hurt her."

He couldn't restrain his grin. One more chance.

Chapter Twelve

Barbara filled the teakettle, placed it on the stove and turned on the gas. Staring sightlessly out the window into the dark night, she started as the whistle of the kettle filled the air. Pouring the water into her teacup, she moved away from it restlessly. Forgetting the drink, she wandered into the next room. It seemed unbearably empty.

The vise on her heart tightened. How could he have done it? And why? The questions circled in her brain, unanswered, tormenting her every thought.

Taking a ragged breath, she reached out to touch the bandanna lying on the counter, the one he had placed around her forehead that first weekend. Crushing the material in her hand, she brought it to her lips to stifle the cry that rose inside.

What had she done to deserve such pain? To lose the man she loved, not once, but twice. Unfairness gripped her, paralyzed her. Sheer will alone forced her to show up in court each day, shutting him out, focusing only on the case. Knowing she was shell-shocked, she knew she wasn't performing up to caliber. But Kenneth wasn't, either.

Correction, Billy.

Thousands of questions chased around to torment her. The how, the why. Who was he really?

It struck her suddenly that she had never called him Kenneth. Had she somehow known all along that he was Billy, not Kenneth?

Dismissing the notion, she pressed her fingers to the nagging pain that centered in her forehead. Of course she hadn't known.

Had she?

BARBARA COLLECTED her briefcase, stuffing some last-minute papers inside, those stored in a folder that rested in the front seat of her car. To her surprise, her client had broached the idea of settlement yesterday.

Just days before he'd been vehemently set against anything but a full-fledged court battle. She had seen the two cookie giants engaged in corridor talk, but she hadn't possessed the courage to join in the discussions with Kenneth standing close between the men.

Considering how close she could be to botching the case, it would be a relief to have a settlement. Not to mention ending the torment of seeing Kenneth each day. Even though she successfully managed the appearance of ignoring him, she was aware of every nuance, every movement, every word he spoke.

Slamming the car door behind her, she forced herself to move forward. She dreaded facing Kenneth over the conference table. She preferred speaking to the judge, her client, anyone but the man who had crushed her heart, stolen her last glimmer of hope.

Purposely straightening her shoulders, she refused

to let any of those feelings show as she strode confidently down the corridor, hesitating only as she reached the conference room. Despite her pose, inside she was staggering. Pushing open the door, she glanced quickly around the room.

And met three pairs of male eyes. Her client, Pete Delight, watched her carefully. As did his opponent, Alexander Matthews, chairman of the Bakewell Corporation.

But it was Kenneth's expression that caught and arrested her attention. It took all of her concentration to ignore him.

Plunking her briefcase on the table, she drew a deep breath and forced her voice to be cool and dispassionate.

"Gentlemen, I hope I didn't keep you waiting. I have the latest draft of the proposal we discussed."

Pete Delight patted the chair beside him and she took a seat.

"I think the terms are going to change considerably," Mr. Delight spoke as he pointed to Alexander Matthews. "This old reprobate seems ready to settle without fighting every issue tooth and nail. Never thought I'd see it in my lifetime."

"Never thought you'd admit to stealing my girl," Matthews retorted, but without malice this time.

Kenneth intervened. "When Lila—Mrs. Delight— had dinner with the gentlemen last night, she explained that her choice in suitors hadn't been swayed by Pete, but by her father. Seems he was the one encouraging Mr. Matthews's attention. Her father thought Alexander could get her to settle her flighty ways."

Barbara raised surprised eyebrows at all three men, even though she knew their history. The two men had once battled for the attentions of the same woman, the woman who had chosen Pete Delight over Alexander Matthews.

However, the prior evening Mr. Matthews admitted that he hadn't exactly pined away for Pete's wife, but that he'd felt tricked by his old friend and business competitor, Pete Delight.

Having reached a truce, they all seemed ready to settle the past. Now it was simply a matter of ironing out contract violations and future negotiations.

Barbara was stunned. She'd expected the negotiations to drag on for weeks, and certainly not on this amicable level. Narrowing her eyes, she wondered what Kenneth was up to. Knowing she would have to examine every word, every phrase in the documents, she kept her thoughts to herself for the moment. If he'd pulled anything funny, she'd find out soon enough.

As the meeting continued, Kenneth wondered if the settlement would thaw Barbara at all. She seemed determined to ignore him. But he was equally determined to break through those barriers. He'd labored over the settlement, hoping it would pave the way with Barbara.

As Pete Delight and Alexander Matthews slapped each other on the back and called each other ornery horse thieves and other terms of endearment, Kenneth slipped over to Barbara's side. But he didn't see an inch of softening there.

Her expression was chilly, dismissive as she

clicked the locks on her briefcase. "I'll fax you a revised draft."

"Barbara, I—"

"I'll have Dani contact you if there are any questions." Spinning on her heel, she exited the room.

Staring after her, Kenneth knew it was time for drastic measures, and setting his jaw, he determined to take them.

BARBARA FINALLY ADMITTED the fatigue that had been eating away at her. Lack of sleep, forgetting to eat, a heart so heavy it continued to drag her down like the anchor of a battleship, all had combined to shred her defenses.

Leaving her office late, she'd brought home a briefcase full of papers. Hoping to lose herself in work, she'd jammed case files and notes in the portfolio with a vengeance. But she suspected even that couldn't distract her.

Twilight descended on the tree-lined avenue, showing promise of the crescent moon that battled with wispy mists of clouds. It was an evening for dreams, for lovers. Barbara choked back the thought as she locked her car and stepped onto the sidewalk.

The shadows seemed to merge. Suddenly one rose and blocked her path. Looking up, she gaped at Kenneth. She tried to push past him when he grabbed her arm.

"I've been trying to reach you, Barbara. The settlement's in jeopardy."

His words penetrated and she stared at him stupidly. "But what happened? When we left yesterday—"

Holding her elbow, he guided her to his car, ushering her inside. "I thought it was all settled, too. But those hardheads are threatening to blow everything apart."

She searched her tired brain while trying to insulate herself against his presence. "Where are we going?"

He had pulled out into traffic. "To the scene of the crime, as they say."

She stared at him blankly. "What?"

He accelerated, moving toward the entrance to the freeway. "Pete and Alexander are planning to duke it out in Las Vegas where Pete and Lila eloped. If we can reach them in time, we can prevent the entire deal from collapsing."

Barbara clutched the door handle, trying not to let the woodsy smell of Kenneth's after-shave or the distinctly male scent that was his alone penetrate her numbed senses.

His presence overwhelmed the car, diminished the space inside. Drawing herself up, she used her other hand to clench her briefcase, feeling as though it were the last sane lifeline to an otherwise insane situation.

"Isn't it a long drive to Vegas?" she asked, as they entered the freeway.

"Too long," he replied briefly. "I've chartered a plane."

"What? You *assumed* I'd be willing to get on an airplane with you?"

He clenched his jaw, a small tick betraying him. "Would you prefer a long drive with me? Six or seven hours from now would put us getting into town past the witching hour."

She stiffened immediately. "I would prefer to keep

the time we're forced to be together as short as possible.''

He winced, then shrugged. ''Then the airplane it is.''

She fumed silently. If she hadn't been so tired when he'd approached, she'd have had the sense to get into her own car instead of being trapped in this narrow space with him. Still, she couldn't give up the last word. ''I want to make myself perfectly clear. The *only* reason I'm going with you is for the sake of my client. Otherwise—''

''I'd just as soon not know in detail exactly how you'd like to dismember me, Counselor. Might ruin my appetite, and I've ordered an excellent dinner.''

She snorted indelicately.

He shrugged again. ''Suit yourself. Since it's a charter flight, the food will be decent. I'm not planning to starve myself.''

Of course not. She'd hate for him to be inconvenienced, to feel a shred of discomfort. Forget the pain she'd felt.

Her raw hurt was giving way to the need to strike back.

Remaining stiffly upright, she tried to melt into the car door as they continued the ride in silence. It didn't take long to reach the airport. Even less time to find their plane.

Stepping outside, she didn't wait for him to open her door. Instead, she moved forward on the tarmac, relishing the crunch of the gravel on the blacktop beneath her shoes, reconnecting her with normality.

Rubbing her elbows, she savored the brisk evening air, the cool tang against her cheeks. She credited a sting of tears to the wind that swept across the runway.

Dashing her hand quickly to her face, she steadied herself. After all, it was only one evening. A short plane ride to settle the case. Then he was gone. Out of her life.

Forever.

Why did that make her feel so bleak, rather than relieved?

She reached for anger, but found only regret.

Turning toward the plane, she took a step forward. Something bright and shiny caught her eye. Automatically she bent to pick it up, a penny so dazzling and gleaming, it appeared to be polished. Closing her eyes, she squandered her wish.

Hadn't she done nearly the same thing earlier? Wished for her life back with Billy? Only, this time, she added that she wished it could have worked. Somehow.

It was hopeless, she knew. Still she slipped the coin into her pocket before walking forward to board the plane. Swallowing the lump in her throat, she imagined how it might have felt if this trip had been taken before she'd discovered the truth. Before his admission destroyed their budding relationship.

Watching Kenneth speak to the pilot, his casual assurance, the confidence that cloaked him, she resented that easy aplomb. She wanted him to appear wounded, painted with the pain that bubbled inside her. And searching, she greedily latched back on to her anger.

Holding her wrath tight and fast, she took her seat as Kenneth rejoined her, refusing to meet his eyes.

Her fury was justified, she knew. Because he'd made her believe. She could have forgiven nearly anything else. But not that.

She averted her head, glancing out the window at the lights on the runway that sped by, blurring as the plane gained speed. The growing noise of the engines signaled the whoosh of power as the plane lifted into the sky.

The last light clinging to that sky quickly gave way to an encompassing darkness, seeming to shroud them in a closed, intimate space. Barbara would have preferred a commercial flight, one crammed with people. She wouldn't have minded crying babies, cranky toddlers or boring businessmen. Anything but an empty cabin she shared only with Kenneth.

She considered reaching for her briefcase, pretending to bury herself in a tall stack of legal briefs, but she refused to show her disquiet. Instead she concentrated on her anger, keeping it alive to fuel her indignation rather than her pain.

The plane sped westward, leaving Salt Lake City far behind.

Glancing up, Barbara saw an older man approaching with a drink tray. She suspected he was the co-pilot rather than a steward and she pursed herself to refuse the drink. As he neared, she saw a kind smile and crumbled a fraction inside.

Unable to appear rude, she took the offered glass and mumbled her thanks.

"Would you care for a snack?" the man asked, still sounding kind.

Numbly she shook her head, knowing food would nauseate her.

"It's been a long time since lunch," Kenneth reminded her quietly as he took the wine bottle from the other man.

"This will be over soon enough," she replied cryptically, praying it would in fact be over before her control dissolved.

"More wine?" Kenneth asked, filling her glass before she could respond.

"Still making decisions for others without hearing their answers, I see." Swirling the wine in her glass, she grasped the fragile stem so firmly her fingers whitened.

"Would it have made a difference?" he asked, knowing neither of them spoke of the wine.

She set her jaw. "I guess you'll never know, will you?"

"And that was my mistake," he admitted freely.

Refusing to meet the entreaty in his eyes, she shifted away to stare blankly out the window. "I don't have anything more to say."

Head averted, she didn't see the struggle on his face before he complied with her request.

Fighting relentless waves of pain, she kept her stiff position intact until the plane began its landing preparations. Automatically she unbuckled her seat belt. The flight had been longer than she'd expected. But perhaps that was because she'd been so intensely aware of every moment.

Deplaning, Barbara glanced around, expecting to see the low deserts of Nevada. Disoriented, she looked again. Then, halting, stared at the sweep of ocean, the cradle of mountains. Infuriated, she whirled around, meeting Kenneth nearly nose to nose.

"What's the idea, Gerrard? I'm no navigational whiz, but even I can tell this isn't Vegas."

"We're at the Monterey Peninsula Airport," he answered with ease. He lifted one hand and pointed. "Carmel's over there."

Fury strengthened her voice, flattened her pain. "What the hell are we doing here instead of Vegas?"

"I guess you'd call it a tactical maneuver."

She considered launching herself at him and giving in to the urge to pummel him. "A *what?*"

"You wouldn't let me come to you." He gestured with a wide sweep of his arms. "So I've brought you to me."

"There's no glitch in the settlement," she accused, hot with anger. "You made that all up just to get me here."

"It worked," he replied evenly.

"Not for long," she retorted. Stomping away from him, she looked for an office, a hanger, anything that would get here out of this airport, back home and away from Kenneth. The torment of seeing him had reached inescapable proportions. She had to stop it now. Spotting the ticket counter, she sped toward it.

But her relief quickly turned to frustration.

The helpful woman behind the counter smiled sympathetically, but firmly. "Yes, ma'am. I'm *sure* there isn't another flight out to Salt Lake City tonight. However, we have several flights early tomorrow."

"There must be *something*," Barbara muttered, unwilling to give up, knowing she couldn't spend another secluded minute with Kenneth.

The woman's smile was patient. No doubt she'd

been through the same drill thousands of times. "Would you like a brochure of the local hotels?"

Accepting the slick paper, Barbara barely contained a groan. She wanted away from Kenneth's home turf. Far away.

Gripping her briefcase tightly, she scanned the lot for a cab. Instead, Kenneth cruised up in a late-model Rover.

Quickly exiting the car, he skirted the hood, then opened the passenger door. "At least let me drive you."

"I'll take a cab," she forced out between stiff lips. They both knew he'd won the first round. She couldn't get back to Salt Lake tonight, but she didn't have to see him anymore. She simply wanted an anonymous driver to whisk her away, make her escape good.

He glanced helpfully up and down the length of the drive. "No cabs."

She started to protest, then remembered how sure she'd been that she could get a flight. Rather than look any more foolish, she got into his car, ramrod straight, staring ahead without looking at him.

He didn't wait for any further confirmation, instead closed the door for her and quickly got back into the car. The practical Rover sped into the darkness as she pulled out the brochure on local hotels.

"Please drop me at the La Playa Hotel," she stated with frigid politeness.

"Hmm," he replied, selecting a CD and putting it in the player.

Unexpectedly, rock music filled the vehicle, startling her. She'd expected something soft and romantic, something he thought might set the mood. Instead, the music was hot and fast.

It was music designed to make the blood heat, then thrum rapidly, like electricity through molten wires.

The comparison struck her as she slanted a glance at Kenneth. Gone was his complacent easiness, replaced by smoldering intensity.

The road he took veered off the main street, seeming to lead away from the cluster of lights in the city. They were climbing. She wondered about the hotel being so remotely located, opened her mouth to question him, then closed it as quickly. It didn't matter to her what route they took to the hotel. The less she had to talk to him, the better.

Carmel Valley opened up in front of them like a dark, magical jewel. Barbara could see towering groves of ancient redwoods outlined in a silver bath of moonlight flanking the curving road. The rise of the mountains surrounded the valley, nestling it securely.

Kenneth turned on an unmarked road. No lights encroached on the gathering darkness. Remote, unapproachable, it didn't look like the road to a hotel. She had picked a practical hotel in the heart of Carmel. Not one that should resemble a hidden resort.

Suspicion bloomed like the night-flowering evening primrose that dotted the hills.

Her voice was flat. "Where are we going, Gerrard?"

He pulled into a driveway that swerved upward sharply. "Here."

Here was a multilevel house that straddled the hill, taking advantage of its natural diversity to create an architectural delight. But Barbara was anything but delighted. Her eyes swept over the redwood-and-stone exterior, the seeming acres of glass windows that no doubt were lit during the day by plentiful sunshine, the wild rush of garden that could be seen in the floodlights flanking the house.

"This isn't my hotel, Gerrard."

"No." His voice was heavy, filled with emotion. "It isn't."

"I'm not going inside." Resolutely she stared at the house, the car door, anything but him.

"We need to talk, Barbara."

"There's nothing to say."

His eyes were somber, reflective. "There's a lifetime of misunderstanding to talk about."

"Are you taking me to my hotel?" she asked again, forcing the desperation from her voice. "Or do I walk?"

Chapter Thirteen

Grudgingly she admitted to herself that his house was exquisite. Open beamed ceilings towered toward the mountains, a full two stories high, giving the house light and enough space to lose oneself in. It was a house she also suspected he didn't share with many people. There was a deep sense of privacy here. One that nearly matched the owner's.

Despite walls of windows and French doors that opened to numerous decks and patios, she sensed few people looked inside these glass barriers. Meticulously maintained, the house flourished with greenery, the planked wooden floors gleamed and the blend of traditional furniture scattered with antiques shone with a polish that tinged the air faintly with lemon.

Her bravado had deserted her when she recalled the miles of darkness between his house and the town of Carmel, knowing she had no innate sense of direction. She didn't want to stumble about all night in the unrelieved blackness. Instead, she had rigidly allowed him to escort her inside.

Soft lamps and a now-crackling fire had banished the gloom. It was a house designed to soothe and envelop. But Barbara, hugging her anger, wanted neither comfort.

"This seems like an awfully far drive from your office in San Francisco," she commented as Kenneth rustled around in the next room.

"I have an apartment in San Francisco for the weekly grind, but this is home," he replied as he entered the spacious den.

Not in the mood for any more chitchat, she stared out the vast windows into the darkness rather than answering.

"Wine?" Kenneth offered, approaching her with a glass.

Mutely she shook her head. She knew the constriction in her throat would choke her.

"I haven't drugged it," he said dryly. Then shrugging, turned and emptied the glass himself. Shoving a hand through his hair, he dislodged the immaculate styling.

It occurred to Barbara that he looked far different this way. Wilder, leaner. More reminiscent of her Billy.

Pain clutched at her, cracking her heart as an ache the size of Texas formed in her throat. Oh...Billy...

He turned then, narrowing his gaze. "Still comparing, I see."

It wasn't fair that he could still read her thoughts. She had done her best to close them down, shut him out.

"You've tricked me into coming here. But this little *kidnap* maneuver won't last long. I won't be falling into your plans, or whatever game it is you're playing now."

His eyes deepened in challenge. "Don't you want to know about that game, Barbara?" He stepped closer, diminishing the space between them, dominating the remaining interval. "Don't you want to know what became of Billy? How I came to be?"

Assaulted by confusing thoughts, she was torn by the tugging desire to know and the stubborn pride that dictated she should walk away. He'd obviously never loved her and that made a mockery of a time she regarded as special. A once-in-a-lifetime kind of special.

Still it was sadness rather than anger that coated her words. "I'm not sure it matters. Billy really is gone forever. I don't even have that hope anymore." Embarrassed that she'd revealed more than she intended, her voice turned brisk. "It's time I left those memories behind."

His hand reached out to touch her cheek. "Maybe not."

"You lied. You've been lying since the trial began...perhaps ever since we met."

"I don't blame you for feeling that way." His thumb eased down her cheek and she didn't pull away. "But things aren't always as they seem."

"And this?" She swept her hand toward the house, raging suddenly. "This wasn't another of your tricks? Bringing me here, trying to turn things around so they're to your advantage?"

His hands came down on her shoulders, abruptly stopping her ranting, the restless swinging of her body. "I couldn't say goodbye without you knowing the truth."

Goodbye. It echoed relentlessly in her mind, staggered her heart. She knew it was so, but the finality stabbed her again.

Shadows crept over the clean, white walls and inevitably over them both, as well. Now that she knew his true identity, she wondered how she hadn't recognized him immediately. Did he wonder, as well?

He reached out to tuck her hair behind one ear. "I'm glad you're still leaving it down."

Unconsciously, she reached to touch her own hair, then let her hand fall away. "It's nothing."

"It is to me," he murmured. "You were so terribly proper before."

Protests formed, then trailed away. He was right. She wasn't the same woman she'd been when he had reentered her life. She busied her hands with her scarf.

Kenneth lifted it off and away.

She wouldn't let him seduce her from her anger. Even though he stunned, overwhelmed and staggered her, she wouldn't let him play on that weakness. Deliberately she stepped back and away.

"If I must stay here tonight, you could show me to my room." Her voice could have iced an erupting volcano, sending the lava shivering back inside for cover.

Kenneth's own voice was clipped. "I'll show you. But don't think we're through, Barbara." His eyes met hers, daring her to disagree. "Not by a long shot."

She followed him down a wide corridor with high ceilings and walls filled with incredible photographs set in exotic locales. The wilds of Alaska competed for space with Barbados and Singapore. Seeing her stare at them curiously, he explained. "My sister's work."

"It looks like she's tried to capture the entire world on film."

"It was her way of coping."

Barbara itched to ask him the meaning of that cryptic statement. Was he alluding to something he, too, had been forced to cope with? She didn't ask, instead trailing him silently. Reaching the room, he pushed open the door and she withheld a gasp. Planning to be critical, she hadn't expected such a lovely wisp of a room.

Sheer, white cotton billowed from the drapes at the French doors and over the cherrywood columns of the four-poster bed. The highly polished wooden floor was softened with rugs of matching flawless white. The room was a dream. And something she hadn't expected to find in this masculine home. Was there a woman in his life? Someone permanent? Barbara whirled around, the question in her eyes, tripping on the tip of her tongue.

Once again he read her thoughts as clearly as though she'd spoken aloud. "It's for my sister on her rare visits. A home base, so to speak."

"And what identity has *she* assumed?" Barbara finally managed, unable to reconcile who he had become, the big chunks of his life that remained secret.

Hurt flickered over his face, then disappeared. "You'll find everything you need in here—towels, a bathrobe, toiletries, the essentials." Turning, he left her.

She told herself she was glad. She wanted to be on her own. Investigating the adjoining bathroom, she found more than mere essentials. Cosmetics and toiletries graced the white tile counters. Wandering back into the bedroom, she found a closet full of clothes. For someone who only rarely visited?

Abruptly Barbara slumped on the bed. What *had* happened to change Billy and apparently his entire family?

Restless, she decided to soak in the tub and hopefully banish all the nagging questions. She poured in a generous amount of gardenia bath salts and slid inside the oversize tub.

But even after a long, leisurely soak, she found herself back in the bedroom, not settling in as she'd told Kenneth she would, instead feeling restless, anxious. Pacing the confines of the room, she found she didn't want to be alone in the bedroom. She wanted to investigate, to leave this solitariness behind.

Rising, she walked to the French doors, seeing only darkness beyond the depths of the terrace. She felt caged, especially when the person with all the answers was in one of the adjoining rooms.

Belting the terry-cloth robe securely, Barbara eased open the door and padded into the hall. Woodsmoke drifted through the air, combining with the aroma of freshly ground coffee beans, and the honeyed scent of the wildflowers she'd spotted outside. Cautiously she approached the huge living area and saw that the doors were pushed open to the outside, accounting for the smell of fresh flowers. The fire snapped as it fed greedily on the air supply that blew softly through the doors.

The room was simple, elegant, yet unrevealing. No family pictures decorated the mantel or the ebony grand piano that brazenly dominated the room. Seeing the room was empty, she skimmed by the bookcases, searching. No scrapbooks or yearbooks littered the shelves. Nor were there any framed diplomas near his desk. It was as though he were a man with no past.

"Seen enough?"

Barbara whirled around, a guilty flush heating her cheeks. "You weren't here when I came in."

"One of the best times for snooping."

She pulled herself upward in a defensive posture. "You said you brought me here to explain."

Something flickered in his eyes, then died. "And you've already made up your mind. Because you're hoping I won't be able to pull off a good enough explanation, aren't you?" He crossed the room. "Because nothing can explain away the years of hurt, or the silence." His eyes hardened, even as remorse traced a visible path. "Well, you're right, Barbara. There is no explanation good enough. No excuse that will diminish your pain or your sense of betrayal."

With all words trapped hopelessly in the dry well of her throat, she simply stared.

He lifted one hand toward her, then let it fall to his side. "Laughter was always my crutch, and there's not a chance in hell that I'm going to laugh you through this one. No humorous antidote or ridiculous act that will make you forget the last fifteen years." Grim lines of regret etched themselves near his mouth even as his lips curved in a parody of a smile. "For what it's worth—I *am* sorry." Giving in to impulse, he cupped her chin. "But I thought it was worth the risk."

Questions tumbled through her head, each racing

to outstrip the other. "What *did* happen?" she asked softly.

Irony tainted his laughter, along with a hollowness. "I was sure you'd never ask."

Impatience battled with concern as she stared at him. "I want to know…I *need* to know."

Dragging both hands through his hair, he turned to the bar, pouring two tumblers of whiskey, offering her one. She sensed his gesture meant the story was going to take more than a gentle glass of wine.

She took a gulp of the Irish whiskey. It tasted of fire. She wondered if the story would, as well.

Silence brewed between them as the tension flared.

"You know what happened that night," he began, not needing to identify which night. The memory was strong, piquant, one neither of them could forget. "But I didn't know what I was going home to."

Time faded away as he recalled the painful evening and began relating it to Barbara.

HE'D BEEN FURIOUS when Barbara had rejected his plan to elope. Even though he had planned everything perfectly, she had poked holes in every strategy with her unfailing logic. They needed little more than each other to live. At least he thought so. She, on the other hand, had pointed out every practical pitfall. Yet he ached with the love he had for her, knowing there would never be anyone he would love as much, regardless of her stubbornness.

Storming toward the dormitory, he'd been taken aback by his brother's sudden appearance. His older brother had offered no explanation, simply overpowering him and pushing him inside the car, then speeding away.

"What the hell's got into you, Josh?" Billy shoved his long, blond hair from his face. "You got something to say, spit it out."

Josh took his eyes from the road for a moment. "I wish it was that easy." And he remained steadfastly silent through the remainder of the ride, despite Billy's demands and eventually taunts. Finally Billy lapsed into sullen silence, vowing to even the score when they reached their destination.

Josh pulled up to the gates that led to the front of the family home, pushed the remote and drove up the circular driveway.

Billy stared at the quiet-looking house, then turned in anger, his hands thrown upward in an eloquent shrug, but Josh interrupted, his voice quiet, heavy. "I'm sorry, Billy. Let's go inside."

Something in his brother's voice sent a frisson of fear skittering up his spine and lodging somewhere near his heart. Whatever was wrong was serious. Anxious to find out, he ripped the door open and loped across the always-immaculate lawn. Before he could reach the front door it opened and a stranger stood just inside.

Halting, Billy glanced around for Josh and found him close behind. His father was a self-made man, who one had gone leaps and bounds beyond anyone's expectations, building a small business into a multi-million-dollar enterprise. Billy thought instantly of kidnapping, extortion....

Josh's hand dropped heavily on his shoulder. "Everyone's in the study."

Terror leapt momentarily into his throat; then he shook aside the notion. His father, Thomas Duncan, had taught him to fear no man. And Billy was confident his father had things under control.

Together Billy and Josh stepped into the room. It struck Billy at that moment how wrong everything seemed, out of kilter. It was as though he'd stepped into another world. Strain and tension filled the comfortable room instead of the ease and laughter that usually resided there.

His mother sat in one of the wingback chairs, his father standing next to her, flanking the sofa where his sister sat carefully curled up, everything in her stance defensive. From the corners of the room, he could see movement—all on the part of strangers.

"Billy, come sit down." His father's tone matched that of his brother's and Billy looked wildly at Josh for support and saw only the heavy lines of worry etched near his mouth.

"Dad, are these people—"

"They're here for our protection."

For the first time Billy noticed the bourbon glass in his father's hand, the fingers clenched tightly around it, whitened to the knuckles. The father he knew needed no one's protection. Reflexively he moved forward.

Thomas Duncan sighed, then stroked his free hand over his wife's shoulder. "I witnessed a murder, son, and it's something I can't walk away from."

Billy spoke impatiently, not understanding why his father's sense of duty should stir the family so, or concern these strangers. "Of course not, Dad—"

His father held up one hand, stemming the expected flow of words. "It's not that simple. The people involved are in organized crime. And they want to tie up loose ends."

A man stepped from the shadows, suddenly dominating the room. "And those loose ends are the Duncan family. Everyone else here has been briefed. In order to protect your lives, it will be necessary for all of you to disappear."

Disappear?

But the man was still speaking. "New names, new identities and, of course, relocation."

His head spinning, Billy stared for a moment before bursting out. "Duncans don't run! They stand and fight!" He turned to his father for affirmation, but saw the heavy veil of regret in his eyes. "We don't run," he repeated, hearing the words echo in the quiet room.

"If you stay, you'll simply all be eliminated," the man said quietly. There was no hint of apology in his voice, only a finality that was slowly beginning to seep in.

Billy turned from his father to his brother. But Josh wore a heavy look of acceptance, as well.

"Even if Dad refused to testify, chances are we'd be killed because we're a loose end," Josh told him dully. "We have no other choice."

Having been raised to believe he had a world of options at his fingertips, Billy couldn't comprehend that they'd all been snatched away in an instant.

His mother rose unsteadily, but she kept a firm grip on her voice. "It means we have to break up the family, Billy. To alter it enough that it won't be recognizable."

"I'll be working on the East Coast," Josh told him.

"And your sister's going to finish school in Paris," his mother inserted.

Billy felt something inside him shatter as his family was being ripped apart.

"We'll move to Washington State," his father added. "Your uncle Albert has agreed to take over the business."

Billy had spoken to his parents the previous day. The events of the past mere twenty-four hours now staggered him. And the idea of his father abandoning a business he'd spent his life building was incomprehensible. "But how—"

"We have to move quickly," the agent inserted. "There won't be time to pack more than a suitcase. I suggest you concentrate on family mementos and pictures since clothing can be replaced. You must all leave by morning."

It occurred to him that no one mentioned where he would be going. He met his father's unblinking gaze.

"Admission to Harvard has already been arranged, Billy."

He thought of how far away the prestigious school was from Houston, from Rice University, from the woman he loved. He had a million other questions, but knew only one issue in addition to his family's safety was paramount. "I can be packed in an hour. Right now I've got to find Barbara."

"You can't do that," his father said quietly.

Outrage clouded his youthful face. "What do you mean?"

"Exactly what I said, son. We can't tell anyone

that we're being taken into the Witness Protection Program. The risk is too great.''

''Barbara's not a casual girlfriend,'' he protested, thinking of his proposal, then his ultimatum.

''Are you willing to jeopardize your entire family's safety…as well as Barbara's?''

Injustice simmered along with a flood of hot words, but the sober, anguished look on his father's face stopped him. Slowly he gazed around the room, his eyes resting on each loved face. His mother's worry was clear as she gazed at him. His brother and sister, looked much as he felt. They were all being ripped away from what they loved.

His gaze returned to his brother. ''Susan?'' he asked, thinking of the woman who'd snared Josh's affection, one they all assumed he would marry.

Slowly Josh shook his head.

Stunned, Billy stared back. She, too, was to be left behind with everything familiar and dear.

The agent cleared his throat. ''This is a great shock for all of you. But the only way the program can work is complete and total separation from your former lives. This includes relatives, friends, business acquaintances. What your father said is completely true. To involve anyone else is to put their life in danger. While it might seem cruel to disappear, it would seem a worse disservice to jeopardize a life.''

Billy felt the sinking truth slam him in the chest. The words he'd casually thrown out to Barbara mocked him. *''Marry me now, Barbara or it's over.''*

Meeting his parents' gaze, he knew there was no choice. Still he raged, his youth and passion unchecked. "I can't leave her behind, as though she means nothing! You don't understand!"

"We understand far too well, son." His father pinned him with the gaze that had always commanded obedience and respect. "It is, of course, your choice. Are you willing to risk Barbara's life and those of your brother and sister?"

Choking on the rage that consumed him, Billy turned on his heel and ran upstairs to his old room. He wanted to rail, to rant against this incredible unfairness. Instead, he felt a terrible death inside. A death of youthful hope and unending optimism. He knew in that instant life would never be the same again. And the changes were just beginning.

KENNETH SWALLOWED HARD against the memories even as he replayed them for Barbara. Her face, a study of growing disbelief and concern, mirrored a host of emotions.

"That's why no one at school knew where you'd gone," she whispered.

"We left everything behind," he replied, unable to disguise the bitterness, the sense of injustice that could still overwhelm him. "And life has never been the same for any of us. My brother never found anyone to replace Susan. The few women he decided to trust found they didn't love him enough to leave everything behind and join his anonymous life." He brooded as he thought of his older brother, always alone, still searching. "We had to break up the family so it didn't resemble the Duncan unit. That meant one person here, two somewhere else, but never all of us living together in the same city. That traumatized my sister and she's been on the run ever since.''

"The photos from around the world," Barbara surmised aloud.

"We can't get together often. It's too risky."

"This many years later?" she questioned, shocked.

"There's no statute of limitations on murder," he reminded her. "And the guy's still behind bars. Even so, he's an influential man, one who'd still like to see my father six feet deep."

"If lives are at stake, why are you trusting me with the knowledge?"

"Because I know you, Barbara."

"This—" she gestured helplessly with her hands "—all sounds so dangerous."

"It is," he replied briefly, not asking for pity, not wanting any.

Barbara shivered in spite of herself and Kenneth smiled sadly. "Anyone who chooses to join with us becomes isolated, as well."

"Are your parents happy?"

He shrugged. "As happy as anyone can be with their family flung to all corners of the globe, destined never to see their children on a regular basis and having given up their life's work."

It was a grim picture. "Do you see them at all?"

A grimace of the inescapable truth tugged at him. "My brother visited me recently."

"Josh was in Salt Lake?" she asked in surprise.

His gaze raked her sharply. "I call him Eric now, but yes, he was there. I was distracted and I hadn't returned my messages. In most families that's simply annoying. For us it can be far more serious."

The unspoken implication was there. *She* had distracted him. His unblinking gaze confirmed the thought.

Barbara flung her hands out in entreaty. "I've seen you laugh, clown around. How is that possible?"

"Because I can't live every moment in fear. If I'm discovered, I'm not going to look back and regret most of my life because I was afraid to really live. I'll look back and be thankful for what I had."

Her eyes were clouded and troubled as she stared at him, hardly able to take in all he'd revealed. It certainly wasn't what she'd expected. "This is very…confusing."

His short bark of laughter was caustic. "It's been confusing since it all began."

The fire burned steadily, yet Barbara could feel a distinct chill. How would it be to spend most of your life running? Not because you'd done something wrong, but because you insisted on standing up for what was right. She remembered the warm, clannish coziness of Billy's family. They had been close, protective of one another and always full of laughter.

"Is that why you don't keep photos around?" A dart of fear clutched her. "In case you are… located?"

He shoved a hand through his hair, and for the first time since their time together, he tugged at the ear that had once held a flashing diamond stud. The old habit must return when he was under extreme stress, she realized.

Abruptly he turned and walked toward the desk, opening a deep bottom drawer and retrieving a leather-bound album. He sank down on the oversize sofa beside her and opened the book.

"It's too difficult to keep them out," he said, his fingers moving over the pictures, touching the familiar faces. "It reminds me of what I no longer have."

Barbara felt a start of moisture gather in her eyes, the constriction of her throat. She glanced down at the happy faces on the first page of the album. These were the Duncans she remembered. Loving and cheerful. The album progressed, a set of happy memories. He continued turning the pages and the pictures changed.

The countenance was more somber now. Strain edged the faces. Even though it had been fifteen years since she'd last seen them, his parents seemed to have aged tremendously. Many of the photos were of one or two family members. Only a few group shots were scattered through the pages.

It was a drastic, telling chronicle. The devastation of the Duncan family. Gone were the happy smiles, the togetherness. It was clear they were isolated from one another and desperately unhappy about that isolation.

Horrified, Barbara did her best not to cry. But a tear escaped unchecked, sliding down her cheek. "It's all so terribly unfair!"

His jaw clenched. "It's something I've had to come to terms with. My father did the right thing, and sometimes that's harder to deal with than walking away. But I wouldn't have had him choose any differently. Someone has to stand up for what's right—regardless of the cost." His hand closed over hers. "But I do regret that you were hurt needlessly."

Her fingers curled softly within his hand. "Why did you take the case, knowing you'd see me?"

"That's *why* I took the case," he replied simply. "I had to know if you were happy. Then I planned to walk away."

"And now?"

"Now it's not that easy."

Barbara took a ragged breath. She felt over-whelmed, staggered by everything he'd revealed. And she wondered how different their lives would have been if she'd said yes, come with him that night. They'd have been together when Josh found him and she'd have been part of his life. Still... There was one question, one critical answer she needed. "Why did you wait to tell me this time?"

The fragrant air still wafted inside, the fire burned steadily. Kenneth stood abruptly, pacing the oak floor. "There's no easy answer to that, Barbara."

"But I want one," she replied quietly.

"Could we walk?" he asked, holding out a hand to her.

Nodding reluctantly, she rose on her own, seeing the flare of pain on his face as his hand dropped to his side.

His jaw ticked as he reached for his car keys. "Let's drive down to the beach. I do my best walking there."

THE SAND MADE a soft, giving carpet beneath their feet as they picked a trail up the magnificent beach. In the darkness, the surrounding trees lent a mystic air as the moss draped elegantly over far-flung branches.

Kenneth squatted down to retrieve a bit of driftwood, turning to stare into the ebony panorama. An oil derrick, decked out in full lighting, resembled a fairy ship. He pointed it out to Barbara as he rose. "A deceptive illusion," he said finally, unable to keep the agony from his voice.

Barbara raised her head to follow his gaze and her beauty struck him again. "Deception is easier for some to see than others."

The tic in his jaw tightened. "I never intended to deceive you, Barbara."

"You just thought you'd argue a case with me, disrupt my ethics…make love to me…and then walk away?"

"I thought I could see that you were happy, fulfilled. And then, yes, I was going to walk away." He lifted a hand to touch her hair. It was still loose, flowing, and he let his knuckles skim over the length. "But it wasn't that easy. You didn't laugh anymore."

"Laugh?" The word was wobbly, uncertain, and she trembled beneath his touch.

Feeling his own heart tremble—and ache—he pulled her a fraction closer. "You always had more spirit than anyone I ever knew. And back then you were full of laughter and love. But when I met you again, all that was missing. Oh, you were on a fantastic career track, but that was all—your life was two-dimensional." He allowed a small smile to escape. "You were uptight, Barbara, with a veneer tough enough to crack coconuts. I wanted more for you. I wanted you to remember how to have fun, to care about something other than your work."

"You made me care about you," she replied quietly.

"I didn't intend to." His hands absently massaged her upper arms. "I had the crazy idea that I could open you up, bring some laughter into your life and then you'd go on." He lifted one hand to cup her chin. "But then I realized that meant you'd go on with someone else. And even though I knew I couldn't have you, couldn't ask you to make the sacrifice, I couldn't stand the idea of your belonging to someone else."

"And it didn't occur to you to tell me who you really were?"

Exasperation mingled with hurt. "I thought I was more than a name...an eye color...a hairstyle. I thought *you'd* know."

She replied with an equal amount of exasperation. "*How...how* was I supposed to know? I got these strange flashes, bits of memories or recollections, but how was I supposed to connect them to *you?*"

"You were part of my soul," he replied, searching her eyes, hoping she would somehow understand.

"Which makes it harder for me to believe you would wait so long to tell me."

Caught in a trap of his own making, Kenneth stared out at the pounding sea. "I kept getting in deeper and deeper, all the while intending to pull back." He turned back to her, tucking a lock of her hair behind one ear. "And then, believe it or not, I didn't want you to get hurt."

"Too late."

"Is it too late for us?" he asked finally, unable to squelch the question, while knowing he still would never ask her for that ultimate sacrifice. Even though he'd willingly given up everything, it wasn't a request he could make of anyone else. Especially not Barbara, not after he'd hurt her needlessly.

The ocean continued its pull and the moon washed over their faces.

Barbara's expression was shuttered as she turned to him. "I don't know.... I just don't know."

Chapter Fourteen

Barbara stirred as long fingers of sunshine crept through the tall windows and warmed the goose-down comforter that was snuggled around her. The night before she had been sure she couldn't possibly sleep, yet she'd fallen into a deep, dreamless slumber. As she stretched, she realized it had been a healing sleep. And a long one, she discerned with some chagrin, seeing it was nearly nine o'clock.

Padding to the French doors, she flung them open and was rewarded by a tumble of bougainvillea that decorated the terrace. In the daylight, she could see the sweep of Carmel Valley, the incredible view of mountains and ocean.

Wondering suddenly what Kenneth was doing, wanting to see him, she slipped down the hall. Beyond the den was a huge kitchen. Doors opened to a flagstone terrace. Kenneth sat there with a carafe of coffee. He turned, sensing her presence.

She hesitantly walked toward him, tugging at the folds of her oversize terry robe.

"Did you sleep well?" he asked, automatically pouring her a thick mug of steaming coffee.

She accepted it gratefully. "Surprisingly well. My mind blanked out on me."

"Perhaps for the best." He rose. "I'll get our breakfast—it's in the warming oven."

She blinked. He'd made breakfast? She was expecting a serious talk over endless cups of black coffee. Mentally preparing herself to shred her remaining nerves, she didn't know what to say when he brought out a huge tray.

First he handed her a spray of orchids, then whisked a plate in front of her. While she watched, he poured goblets of mimosas. Abandoning her coffee, she sipped the heavenly mixture of champagne and orange juice. Intrigued by the covered plate, she lifted the metal warming lid.

"Blintzes?" she asked in surprise. "You made blintzes?"

A grin tugged at his lips. "Afraid not. But Carmel boasts the best in restaurants." His voice ripened. "I remember how well you liked them on our Orient Express breakfast."

So she had. She swallowed the knot in her throat, remembering the perfection of that day. Knowing he watched her, she forced herself to taste the heavenly combination of crepes, rich filling and obviously homemade strawberry jam.

Enchanted with the picture-perfect setting, she found, despite all that lay between them, that she was able to eat a few bites. "This is quite a change from last night," she commented, sipping her drink.

"I figure I don't have long to win you back. I don't want to waste any time."

Her eyes widened. "That's subtle."

"But true. I'm guessing you're still confused."

She was. Impossibly so. Could she forget the pain he'd caused by not giving her any choice this time? Was there any reason valid enough to destroy her first love, then her trust?

His voice turned brisk. "Then my job's cut out for me. You'll find clothes in the closet in your room. You and my sister are about the same size."

She shook her hair back, preparing her excuses, protecting her battered emotions.

But he was one step ahead. "No stress, Counselor. Let me show you around the area—it's really quite beautiful."

She hesitated. "Is it safe?"

He laughed, that rich café au lait laugh that curled her insides. "Of course. That's the whole point of changing my identity. You didn't see me watching my back in Salt Lake City, did you?"

Good point. "But I thought…"

"It's not entirely grim," he said softly. "If it was, I would never have contacted you."

The beautiful valley and the man who held her heart beckoned. "All right. On one condition. I fly back tonight."

He started to argue, saw the determination in her eyes and relented. "But the rest of the day is mine."

KENNETH TOOK full advantage of their time, plying her with the sights, sounds and wonders of Carmel and Monterey, from the Aquarium to the Cannery to the incredible row of art galleries.

And she loved it all. Yet even as he wooed her, Barbara's thoughts kept rushing toward everything she'd learned since last night. She knew she still couldn't forgive his omission, the way he'd shattered her trust.

The hours spun by, sharpened by the need she felt, by the desperation she sensed in him. It was as though each moment rushed them toward a destiny that couldn't be postponed. The sea drew them at day's end to an uncrowded spot. Gone were the distractions, leaving only all that lay unresolved between them.

The ocean plunged toward the shore behind them. Gray sky melded with the sea, blotting out the horizon. Magnificent moss-shrouded trees lined the beaches. As they walked the length of the pier, the smell of wet hemp mingled with the day's catch and the heady aroma of hot dogs from a sidewalk vendor. It was a piercing array of aromas. Ones she knew she would always remember. Ones she would always link to this day, this man.

Barbara fought the catch in her throat. "Kenneth, I have to get to the airport. I'll just have enough time to catch my flight."

His eyes dimmed and he braced himself against the urge to persuade her to stay. How could he ask her for such a sacrifice? She was right. He had manipulated her since the beginning of the case. He'd stretched her trust and broken it. He couldn't ask for more. As much as he wanted to speak the words crowding on his tongue, instead he tightened the grip on her hand as he searched her eyes. "It's your call, Barbara."

They were quiet as, true to his promise, he drove to his house, picked up her briefcase, then started down the road toward the airport.

Tension slashed between them, a force as vivid as the clouds that rolled ominously from the sea.

"Funny weather," she commented finally in a tight voice. "It was beautiful all day, but now..."

It hit him suddenly. Fog. That was what she was seeing.

"You realize what this means?" he asked, slamming on the brakes and pulling off the side of the road.

She glanced at him suspiciously. "No."

"That's fog, Barbara. You won't be able to fly out tonight."

Jerking her head, she stared out the window. "Are you sure?" she asked weakly. "Maybe it's just rain, or a thunderstorm or a—"

"It's fate, Counselor. Giving us one more chance."

THE FOG SHROUDED the house, enfolding them in an incredibly intimate setting. Barbara didn't even pretend it wasn't affecting her.

Because everything about him affected her. She sat in the study while Kenneth showered. Giving in to the urge that had been nudging her, she reached for the picture album that was still lying on the coffee table.

She leafed through the pages, seeing again the suddenly changed history of the Duncan family. Unhappiness and distress lined all of their faces. How could she have overlooked this heartache? Practically dismissed it as she'd concentrated on how it had affected her, rather than them. True, she'd felt terrible about what he'd revealed, but the enormity of the sacrifice hadn't completely sunk in.

Rocking her, the realization stabbed.

He'd had to choose.

The safety of his family, or her.

Even though he'd told her of being swept into the Witness Protection Program, she hadn't grasped that he couldn't jeopardize his family's safety by including her in their secret.

Having concentrated only on how Billy's disappearance had affected *her,* feeling first abandoned, then betrayed, she realized she hadn't stopped to imagine how he must have felt. Forced to leave his family, friends, school and everything familiar, his life had been ripped away from him.

Everything she took for granted, including his freedom, all had been painfully denied him. By choosing to do the right thing, he and his family had walked a solitary, lonely path, not daring to make new friends, forced to leave behind everything they cherished. Could she have been strong enough to make the same choice? Could she even now?

What would it be like to discover one day you had to throw away your past...yes, even the one you loved? Because she knew with every bit of certainty that she *had* been his love.

She thought of her own family, the casual ease with which they could congregate. Her eyes drifted down to the pain showcased in the photographs in the album. Nothing was easy for the Duncan family. Certainly not for the boy Billy had been, nor the man Kenneth had become. The past had been erased, the future was uncertain.

She stared out the massive windows, listening to the music that played, thinking of how very isolated

Kenneth's life was, how much he risked even now by telling her. He hadn't said so, but he'd placed a huge amount of trust in her hands by divulging the Duncans' secret. Their very existence could be shattered by such knowledge. She *was* important to him, she realized. As important as his own safety.

The catch in her throat grew as the song Kenneth had left to play on the stereo finally penetrated her senses. She listened carefully to the haunting words of the melody he had serenaded her with in the horse-drawn carriage. The song that had been theirs so many years ago, one that had drawn them together in the throes of first love, one that spoke to them again on their precarious second start.

Well into the second verse, the song beckoned. As it concluded, the final words replayed themselves in her mind, words of a young man as he pleaded with his lady not to end their love. Remembering how Kenneth had waged his own campaign to win her back, she was struck by the similarity. Suddenly doubting her stubbornness and the wisdom of her decision, she swallowed a growing lump in her throat.

Sensing Kenneth's presence, she slowly raised her eyes. A loosely belted robe covered his freshly washed body, and his hair was a dark, wet mane. The thatch of hair on his muscled chest gleamed with moisture. His distinctive scent reached her and she could feel the trembling in her limbs…the quaking in her heart.

Just as he had when she was eighteen, he made her feel alive in a way no one before or since had ever accomplished. She thought suddenly of the lucky penny she'd found the night before, the subconscious wish to have him back, for it to work this time.

Unsteadily she rose to her feet, silently beckoning him.

Her eloquent eyes spoke to him. In a few quick strides, he stood next to her. "Barbara?"

She reached out to stroke his jaw. "I'm sorry."

Surprised, he reached for her hand. "For what?"

"For all your pain, for your losing everything dear. For thinking more of what it cost me than what it cost you."

Shaken, he felt his heart lurch.

Then she was in his arms, melting against him. Her hands were greedy, her lips urgent. Afraid to question her change of heart, he accepted the caresses, returned the kisses.

Desperation seized them. Hot, relentless, untamed.

"I should have known it was you," she whispered against his lips, feeling her own tremble with the revelation. "Maybe part of me did."

"I wanted you to know, to reach out and see who I was," he admitted, sinking his face against the soft sweep of her hair. "No one has ever known me as well as you."

Tiny gasps escaped her. "I've missed you. All these years…"

"I love you. I've never stopped loving you," he admitted freely, thankful she was in his arms, praying somehow it would last.

"I want you as much now as then," she confessed, her fingers linking behind his head. "Maybe more."

"You dazzle me, Barbara Callister," he said finally, his breath a whisper against her cheek. "That hasn't changed. That won't *ever* change."

She was in his arms suddenly as he swept her into his embrace, carrying her down the hall, to his bedroom, a room she'd not yet seen. Tendrils of fog-drenched moonlight spilled through the wall of windows, across the lush carpet that he carried her over soundlessly.

This was his world, one she wanted to belong to again.

His lips were endlessly patient, endlessly greedy as they moved over hers, eliciting her approval, sealing her fate. Each movement, each nuance was sweetly familiar now, the past leaving its reckoning print on the present they now shared.

Her heart sang as his hands made a reverent journey over her body and a wall of memories flooded her. Reaching upward, she traced the slant of his jaw, his firm chin, pausing over laugh lines near his eyes, her heart clenching over those of pain etched by his lips. How could she have not seen the signs before? Recognized the strength. With the life he'd been forced to lead, it was little wonder he possessed so much insight and wisdom.

Wishing she could erase that pain, all he'd sacrificed, she sighed against him, then began a journey of her own as his strong, clever hands peeled away the barriers of clothing.

Kenneth looked down into the face that had been part of his irretrievable past and now his future. All the hesitation and reserve was gone from her shadowed features, replaced by a sweetness that sang in his blood, then gripped his heart.

Now he could reveal his knowledge of each pleasure she craved. Slowly, almost lazily, he dipped into the flames she could so easily ignite. Her answering strokes were gentle, warm and totally accepting.

It was that acceptance, that hope, which fueled him. Making her drift on a languorous sweep of pleasure, he reveled as she tilted her throat back to accept each kiss, each savoring taste.

As he took them higher, feeling her shudders of pleasure, her inarticulate gasp of satisfaction, he watched her eyes flicker to a shuttered place. And his heart prayed she had taken him with her.

THE SILVERY CAST of moonlight revealed all of his perfect features. Billy, Kenneth. The man she loved.

Traces of tension still lined his face and she nearly reached out to smooth them away. Slowly she pulled her hand back. She didn't want to awaken him just yet. He'd barely fallen asleep after their hours together.

Slipping from the bed, she donned his terry robe and watched him for another long, silent moment. He nearly stirred, so she crossed the room silently. Making her way soundlessly down the corridor, she entered the den where the banked fire had burned down to a splutter.

The lights were still on, making it easy to find her way. This time she could savor the room, learn more of this intriguing man she intended to call her own. To discover all the changes that accompanied his transformation from boy to man. While she'd grown to know him in his new identity, it struck her that he'd shown her only the smooth, easy pieces of his life. It was clear there was so much more.

Her fingertips drifted over the rows of books that filled the mahogany shelves. So many leather-bound volumes. She wondered if they made up for the lonely gap in his life. Picking up one book, she flipped it open and a picture fell out, slipping to the floor. She picked it up, started to replace it, and then stared at the photo. It was a particularly revealing photo, taken shortly before the Duncan family had been separated. She knew the time frame because she stood next to Billy in the picture. They were laughing, carefree, painfully in love. Both of them looked incredibly happy.

A thought struck her. She, and only she, had the ability to give him back part of that life, a fraction of that happiness. She was the only woman who had known him as he was and who could love him for the man he had become. The only one that could meld both halves of his life. There need be no barriers between them, no secrets to protect the past. They *had* come full circle.

Holding her breath, her fingers caressed the picture once again. Gripping it in that same hand, she crossed the room and stood at the desk. In moments, she was rummaging in the top drawer, trying to find a pair of scissors. Unable to find them, her gaze skipped across the room until it rested on her purse.

Retrieving it, she reached inside, her fingers tripping across the lucky penny she'd stashed. A flash of intuition pierced her and she rubbed the penny one more time. Then she picked up her manicure scissors, carefully cutting Kenneth's picture to fit her locket.

Opening the heart-shaped necklace, she placed the new picture on top of the old one.

Hoping he wanted this piece of his life back as much as she wanted to give it to him, she clasped the locket shut.

The bedroom was still dim when she reentered. The fog had dissipated, leaving a spill of moonlight to drench the open wall of windows and travel over the room. She thought Kenneth was still asleep as she approached the bed. Soundlessly she padded close, unbelted the robe and let it slide to the floor.

"I wondered where you'd gone," he said quietly, a wealth of unasked questions lingering in his husky tones.

His voice didn't startle her. She was glad he was awake. The sheets rustled gently as she rejoined him. "Don't wonder anymore." Taking his hand, she guided it to her locket. "I believe you know all my secrets."

She felt the faintest tremble in his hands as he opened the trick fastening. Glad of the illuminating moonlight, she watched the shadows in his eyes clear as he saw the newly joined pictures.

"I love you," she said simply.

"My life isn't an easy one to share," he warned in a voice threaded with logic and a thrumming of longing.

She laughed then, a rich sound that covered a lifetime of memories, and a fair share of regret. "You've never been easy."

His arms trapped her, rolling her back to the mattress, her face inches from his. "This time I won't let you go."

"This time I'll hold you to that."

His hands lifted to gently fist her hair. "Would you really consider giving up everything to marry me?"

Her smile was equally tender. "Just think of what I'm getting in return."

"A man with no name of his own, a life of duplicity, uncertainty—"

She placed her fingers on his lips, stilling the words. "I've always regretted saying no to you fifteen years ago. I was almost foolish enough to repeat that mistake. But I don't want to live the rest of my life regretting...wondering. I want to spend my days with you—" her eyes darkened to a deep midnight velvet "—and share my nights with you. *I* want your blue-eyed babies, your head on the pillow next to mine, your arms around me, the past we both share."

"Don't think you'll get tired of me in the next fifty years?" he asked, tracing a reverent line along her cheek, his thumb then easing over her lips.

A smile lit her eyes, lingered on her face. "Just think of all the spectacular surprises I'm in for. By the time our golden anniversary rolls around, I think heart-shaped pizzas will pale in comparison to what you'll dream up then."

"Don't think I'll disappoint you?"

She couldn't repress the hitch in her voice, the glistening in her eyes. "Never."

His hands cupped her face, his eyes connecting with and holding hers. "I can't believe we've been given a second chance."

"And maybe this time—"

He stopped her words with a kiss. "No maybes, Barbara. This time is ours. No regrets?"

Her smile reached into her heart. "Not anymore, now that I have you."

"I love you, Barbara Callister."

She thought she heard a sound like a coin clinking to the floor, reminding her of the lucky penny she'd wished on. Dreams did come true. And this time she would share hers with her first and only true love. "And I love you."

Clouds wisped by, casting shadows on the moon, then lifting, taking them away, chasing away the regret. The moon glimmered again. Drifting on the past, cradling the future and shining on the night.

HARLEQUIN®
INTRIGUE

WE'LL LEAVE YOU BREATHLESS!

If you've been looking for thrilling tales of
contemporary passion and sensuous love stories
with taut, edge-of-the-seat suspense—then
you'll love Harlequin Intrigue!

Every month, you'll meet four new heroes
who are guaranteed to make your spine tingle
and your pulse pound. With them you'll enter
into the exciting world of Harlequin Intrigue—
where your life is on the line
and so is your heart!

THAT'S INTRIGUE—
ROMANTIC SUSPENSE
AT ITS BEST!

HARLEQUIN®
Makes any time special ®

Harlequin® Historical

From rugged lawmen and valiant knights to defiant heiresses and spirited frontierswomen, Harlequin Historicals will capture your imagination with their dramatic scope, passion and adventure.

*Harlequin Historicals...
they're too good to miss!*

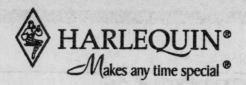